Lucile Morrison
January, 1960.

PARENT-CHILD TENSIONS

Parent-Child Tensions

BERTHOLD ERIC SCHWARZ, M.D.
Diplomate of the American Board of Psychiatry and Neurology

AND

BARTHOLOMEW A. RUGGIERI, M.D.
Diplomate of the American Board of Pediatrics

J. B. LIPPINCOTT COMPANY
Philadelphia

Distributed in Great Britain by
Pitman Medical Publishing Co., Limited, London

Library of Congress Catalog Card Number 57-14865

Printed in the United States of America

TO
ADELAIDE McF. JOHNSON, M.D., Ph.D.

A courageous physician whose pioneering work
has brought a deeper understanding and new hope
to the treatment of the emotional problems of
parents and children.

Preface

It is our hope that the reader may find this book of some value in understanding himself, his family and the significant people in his life. In our desire to reach as wide an audience as possible we have used nontechnical language without avoiding the presentation of sometimes difficult concepts. Some of these concepts are quite new, but they are amply documented in the scientific literature and represent our own experience with patients. In some cases, in our attempt to present as comprehensive a picture as possible, we have included material which a few readers may find upsetting. But the physician, like all scientists, is concerned with facts. He cannot acknowledge some and reject others in conformity with fads and prejudices. Only by recognizing the complete picture as it actually occurs may he really understand the problem and be in a position to offer help to his patient.

We are grateful to our good friend, Rev. Timothy V. A. Kennedy, M.D., who encouraged us throughout the preparation of our manuscript and made many suggestions that helped us to present some of the difficult concepts more lucidly. His suggestions were particularly propitious because of his vast clinical experience as a psychiatrist and his special interest in all the varied forms of delinquent behavior in children and adults. We are also grateful to our friend, Dr. Adelaide McF. Johnson, one of the originators of collaborative study, who generously read our manuscript and offered a number of helpful suggestions in line with her own rich clinical experience. The inspiration for this book lies in the deep and far-reaching influence of two physicians, teachers and friends of unusual wisdom and perspective, Drs. Samuel W.

Hamilton and Louis S. London, whose combined careers span almost a century of psychiatric and psychoanalytic experience. Also found on these pages are the teachings and the wide experiences of Drs. Reginald G. Bickford, David A. Boyd, Lawrence C. Kolb, Magnus C. Petersen and Howard P. Rome, whose diversified interests range from the investigative laboratory to the bedside.

BERTHOLD ERIC SCHWARZ
BARTHOLOMEW A. RUGGIERI

Montclair, N. J.

Introduction

The physician who sees many children in his practice is often impressed by the frequency with which parents bring up emotional problems and by the interest that mothers and fathers show when the physician discusses this aspect of medicine.

"I'm not worried, Doctor, about the treatment of pneumonia or tonsillitis. One shot of medicine and he'll be well. It's the other problems that worry me."

The physician fully agreed with this mother's implied statement that too often the emotional problems of children are not given their proper due. However, he had to disagree with this parent's further implication that one can separate the child's emotional problems from other manifestations of disease. He knew that the line between the child's emotional and physical make-up is very poorly drawn and that both these aspects of the child's make-up are inseparably mixed together. From his experience in diagnosing and treating diseases in children (and adults), he knew that both factors frequently are present in the same child (and adult) and interact to produce the final picture of disease that presents itself to the physician.

The physician knew the scientific folly of attempting to classify symptoms arbitrarily as being due to either emotional or physical causes. Emotional problems may masquerade with symptoms which are entirely suggestive of physical disease. Or, emotional problems may actually lead to a serious physical disability such as obesity or bed-wetting. On the other hand, physical disease may masquerade with symptoms which are entirely suggestive of emotional disease. Examples are brain tumor or an overactive thyroid gland.

By his years of training and experience in the practice of medicine, the physician is well suited to studying and understanding the child as a whole. Only the physician can correlate and get a clear picture of the individual as a whole from the hodgepodge of apparently isolated findings that make up the child: the difficult delivery and the mother's fears of its effect on the baby; the 3-month colic; the age at which he walked; the blood pressure; the heart murmur and the fright that it produced in the child and his parents; the sore throats; the goblins in his nightmares; the polio attack; the taunts of his brother; the battle with his mother during bowel training; the unequal reflexes; and the imitation of his father's swagger.

The following chapters on the interactions of the emotions and the behavior of the child are an outgrowth of many informal discussions during the authors' years of specialty training at the Mayo Clinic and subsequently as neighbors in the private practice of their specialties, psychiatry and pediatrics respectively. Through the years the authors have become increasingly aware of the fact that a thorough understanding of the patient's emotions is indispensable to the total care of the patient, regardless of what branch of medicine the physician may practice.

Man always has been interested in his emotions, how and why he feels, thinks and acts as he does. Since shortly before the turn of the 20th century, the study of man's emotions has been put on a more scientific basis by the pioneering research of many physicians, among whom should be mentioned Sigmund Freud, Carl Jung and Alfred Adler. Despite the far-reaching significance of their findings, the importance of the work of these men is not generally appreciated outside the medical profession. Fifteen years ago, while working together at the Institute for Juvenile Research in Chicago, A. McF. Johnson, M.D., and S. A. Szurek, M.D., first elaborated the therapeutic technic of intensive bilateral or multilateral treatment. This technic is that of collaborative study in which one physician studies the feelings and the behavior patterns of the child while other physicians study the feelings and the behavior patterns of the parents (or parent substitutes) and other children. This is done in hour-long interviews ranging from 1 to 5 a week and lasting over a period of a few months to several years. The physicians meet in weekly or biweekly discussions of the findings of the preceding hours. By such frequent and continued comparison of all the data obtained from the child and the parents, the interaction of the emotions of child and parent becomes clear. In this way, it has been discovered that in almost every case of an emotionally disturbed child, the child's specific disturbed feelings stem directly from specific disturbed feelings in the parents. Through this unique method of study, the physician can pinpoint for the first time the source of the child's emotional disturbances. This method has clarified many previously mysterious and difficult problems and promises to clarify more. As an offshoot of the findings of collaborative study, it has also been found that the physician frequently cannot treat the child successfully without concurrently treating the source of the child's problems—the parents. During the past decade, Drs. Johnson and Szurek have continued their work separately at the Mayo Clinic in Rochester, and the Langley Porter Clinic in San Francisco, and have elaborated their original discoveries. At the present time, this therapeutic approach has become widespread and in fact very much the rule in many of the best clinics in the country.

From the authors' experience with this new technic while on the child psychiatry unit of the Mayo Clinic, they learned certain principles of approaching disease which they then applied in the private solo practice of their specialties. The authors have found this knowledge to be extremely useful in the study of the usual routine problems that make up a physician's everyday practice in addition to the study of the tricky, subtle and rarer problems that find their way to the specialist or the large medical center.

Recognizing the importance of this new information and how it would help to answer the many questions that parents direct to the authors in their everyday private practice, it was felt that there would be a distinct value to writing a book on these problems for the lay public. This information has been shown to be of extreme value not only in the physician's treatment of these disorders but also in the prevention of emotional disturbances.

During the writing of this book, the question arose whether or not to include chapters on topics which are usually considered hush-hush and improper to mention, much less discuss. The importance of this question of including or omitting these subjects from the book was increased by our knowledge that recently developed information on these subjects was of a potentially explosive character. On the other hand, the authors knew that these problems are common in the everyday practice of medicine and have far-reaching and serious effects upon society itself. To dodge a discussion of these important problems when so much is known about them would be weakening the entire purpose of writing this book. Therefore, these subjects have been included, and an honest discussion has been given.

In studying this book with its many illustrative cases from the authors' own personal experience, the reader will discern a consistent pattern of approaching emotional problems. The specific details of each case apply only to that particular case. However, the general method of approach to the problems being discussed (i.e., juvenile delinquency), apply to all cases coming to the physician with that problem. No case is presented in its entirety; no case could be presented in its entirety. In each example are included only the highlights of the many facts gained by the physicians after many hours of painstaking study of the patient and the parents. These examples are offered only to make clear to the reader, through detailed application to an actual patient, the general principles to be learned from a careful study of each type of emotional disturbance discussed. It should be emphasized that these disturbances are unfortunately common; one has only to look for them.

This book should not be construed as an attempt to present all types of and all the known material on emotional disturbances in children. Nor was this book written cookbook style as a handy book of reference or manual in which the reader can look up a subject in the index and then read the material on that subject alone without reference to the rest of the book. The authors recognize that much of the material to be presented could and often does lend itself to skimming over with vague generalizations and honeyed platitudes. However, the authors also recognize that the newer knowledge about these problems is often very difficult for the lay person, with little medical background, to understand. Therefore, this book was written in such a manner that any given chapter can be understood only in the light of all that has been presented in each of the previous chapters. *This book can be understood only if it is read from beginning to end without omission.*

Collaborative study has shown how the specific feelings and behavior of the child are dependent upon the specific feelings and behavior of the parent. Through similar means, the child affects his parents. It has been shown that the emotional experiences of an individual as a child will determine his emotional make-up as an adult. Therefore, this book, which is directed primarily to the problems of the child, should also help to clarify the problems of the adult.

B. E. S.
B. A. R.

Contents

CHAPTER 1

The Mouth Stage

The Child's First Pleasures and Conflicts

The child's emotional growth keeps pace with his physical growth. Any adult who has watched children develop knows that the child's body grows most rapidly during the first 2 years of life, with a second period of rapid growth occurring during adolescence. It is perhaps less well known that the child's brain attains more than three fourths of its adult size by the 2nd year of age. And it is probably least well known that the foundations for the child's feelings and attitudes toward people which will direct his behavior throughout his life are laid down in the preschool years. Emotional growth continues beyond the preschool years, throughout life, but this growth is upon this early foundation. The emotional values and feelings during the preschool years influence all the emotional values and feelings that are acquired later in life. Failure to gratify the simple needs of these early years will sow the seeds for later resentment, insecurity and anger.

The birth cry is the newborn's first response, but any mother will remember that even while in her womb, the baby had had periods of relative activity and inactivity. The physician knows that during this period various hormones and chemicals are constantly being interchanged between mother and child. It has been shown that as early as the 7th month, while inside the mother's womb, the baby's brain is discharging electrical impulses which can be detected by a brain-wave machine. These brain waves have been shown to change when the mother alters her position or when she hears a loud noise. Therefore, things that affect the mother are already being re-

flected in the child's brain before birth. Who knows but that
sometime in the near future medical science will further un-
ravel these mysterious changes and reveal other physical,
chemical and perhaps emotional relationships between mother
and child before birth. However, for the present, any attempt
to discuss what occurs emotionally between mother and child
before birth is pure speculation.

There is a great gap between this first amorphous cry of the
newborn and the precise muscular co-ordination and the many
subtle shades of love and hate emotions of the adult. The baby
is completely helpless and dependent upon his parents. The baby
may cry at this young age, because he is hungry or uncomfortable. He may be in pain, or he may just need love, the feeling
of being warm and physically close to another human being.
The baby learns to love by receiving love.

Mrs. M. wanted a boy very badly, and when a daughter was
born, she had immediate trouble. Nancy was a quiet baby in
the hospital. Nursery rounds rarely found the baby awake.
The 2nd day after discharge from the hospital, Nancy began
crying for long periods at a time, and nothing seemed to satisfy
her. The entire household was in an understandable turmoil.
Mrs. M. frantically telephoned the physician, who came to the
house, examined the baby, and found no evidence of disease.
However, when the physician picked up Nancy and held her
gently in his arms, she relaxed, closed her eyes and fell asleep.
The astonished mother asked, "Do you mean you're supposed
to pick the baby up when she cries?" The physician understood the situation better when Mrs. M., discussing her
methods of feeding the baby, said that Nancy was feeding
herself with a bottle holder. The baby was lacking the physical
and emotional attachment to another human being that she
desperately needed.

"But Doctor, are you supposed to pick up a baby every time
she cries?" If the baby is crying because the diapers are wet,
change them; if the baby is hungry, feed her. Or, the crying
may also be due to gas pains with the crying causing the swal-
lowing of more air and thus increasing the pain. Finally, crying
may simply be crying, a good way for the growing infant to
express her energy and restlessness; she has not yet learned any

other means of expressing herself. Where the older child may jump, sing or run about with the pure joy of life, the young baby cries and thrashes about. From this simple expression of feeling, the infant gradually learns from the parents the innumerable and complex emotional reactions associated with living.

Before the birth of the baby, the doctor usually asks the mother whether or not she plans to feed her baby from the breast or from a bottle. This question has aroused much confusion and emotion, but the answer is really not so difficult. The important point is how the mother feels toward her baby. It does not really matter which method is used. If the mother has adequate breast milk and enjoys breast-feeding, that certainly should be the method of choice. On the other hand, if the mother is unable to breast-feed or does not wish to do so for any one of innumerable reasons, a formula can be substituted without any physical or emotional harm to the baby. If the mother loves her child and the child is healthy, the specific method of feeding is of secondary importance.

The ability to breast-feed depends upon the mother's health, her own feelings of contentment and her innermost sentiments in this matter. If she really does not want to breast-feed, she will be unable to produce milk regardless of what she or the physician may say to the contrary. Sudden fright may stop an already established flow of breast milk. For example, Mrs. B.'s ample supply of milk stopped overnight when her husband was suddenly and accidentally killed.

The child's development progresses from above downward, from head to feet. Thus, he first fixes on some object with his eyes. For example, by 1 month of age, a child will commonly follow a moving light with his eyes through a 90° arc. Next, the child will reach for an object, and eventually, by 4 to 5 months of age, he will succeed in grasping the object, although his grasp at this stage is an extremely awkward one. By about 4 months of age the child plays with his hands, and he eventually manages to place his thumb in his mouth. Even this simple act of development, expected for this age, causes many mothers to turn to the physician for advice. Continuing this downward progression, the baby learns to control his back muscles so that he can sit without support and then masters control of the other parts of his body so that he learns to crawl, stand and finally walk.

Many parents attach incorrect and exaggerated values to thumb-sucking. Mrs. F., with a 5-day old child, surprised her physician one morning when she told him that she had made the nurses place mittens on her baby girl after she "caught" her baby with thumb in mouth.

At this age, when a child's thumb finds its way to the mouth, it is just plain luck. But, Mrs. F. would not listen to her physician; she did not want a thumb-sucker; the mittens had to stay.

A mother need not become concerned with persistent thumb-sucking until the child is about 3 years of age. If the thumb-sucking persists beyond this age, it may be a symptom of some emotional disturbance. The child behaves at a baby-like level when he should be progressing to young childhood. It must be emphasized that although the various phases of emotional development are discussed separately in these early chapters, nature does not place each phase into its own separate niche completely apart from the other phases of development. The mouth phase lasts from birth until the first year of life, it is true, but this only means that during that time the child's main interest and enjoyments come from the mouth. But, interests and enjoyments which come from the mouth do not end abruptly at 1 year of age. After all, many adults still enjoy eating, gum-chewing, smoking, kissing and the like. At one year of age, a new main center of interest and enjoyment normally appears and takes precedence over the earlier interests in the pleasures derived from the mouth (see Chap. 3).

There are circumstances, which will be discussed more fully in succeeding chapters, in which such progress may occur later than expected or in which, even with the appearance of the next stage of emotional development, the great dependence upon earlier means of enjoyment (for example, the mouth) continues as strongly as before.

Carl, at 4 years of age, continues to suck his thumb. He also bites his nails and grinds his teeth. His mother has tried every means to stop thumb-sucking: punishment, cajolery, bribery and painting the thumb with an obnoxious tasting liquid. Carl, contrary to the magazine advertisements, apparently does not mind the taste of this liquid. Or, is it more nearly correct to say that his pleasure from thumb-sucking is greater than his distaste for the liquid? His mother is now even considering placing splints on his arms (so he cannot bend them to place his thumb in his mouth) or attaching a rakelike device to his upper teeth against the hard palate (so that when he tries to suck his thumb, the rake will scrape against his thumb). Such cruel suppressive devices may only increase the desire to suck his thumb. The physician also learned that, from earliest infancy, Carl was not permitted to gratify his natural desire to suck. His mother always made a point of discouraging all thumb-sucking (at an age when this was normally expected), because she feared that this would deform his growing teeth and mouth. The nipple and the bottle were stopped completely at 6 months of age, thus depriving Carl of another indispensable means of enjoying himself through the mouth during the first year of life. Most children will want a bottle and nipple at bedtime anyway until about 2 to 3 years of age. Carl's mother also always pulled out of his mouth anything that was placed there with the exhortation, "Dirty boy!" She was apparently unaware that at a very early age the child learns the shape and the feel of an object as well, if not better, with his mouth than with his hands and eyes. The answer to this problem is therefore more complex than simply saying, "You must not!" or using suppressive measures.

Many mothers fear, from what they have read and been told, that thumb-sucking will deform the teeth. This is not true. More important that the unjustified fear of deforming the teeth should be the justified fear of deforming the child's emotional development by not permitting him to do what is expected for his age and thus depriving him of one of the chief means of obtaining pleasure appropriate for his age.

Nail-biting, teeth-grinding, gnawing on pencils, gum-chewing (and smoking and drinking in adults), with their emphasis upon the mouth as a means of obtaining pleasure and relieving tension, also stem from values related to the mouth stage of development.

Georgie, who is 6 years old, came into the physician's office with a very nervous and worried mother. Georgie had persistent thumb-sucking in addition to numerous other emotional complaints. His mother feared the worst—mental deficiency. The physician's questioning revealed that Georgie held his head up, reached for and grasped objects, crawled, sat up and walked at the expected ages. On careful examination, there was no evidence of any disease. However, the physician, his guard aroused, questioned further and found that Georgie's home life was not ideal. His parents were recently divorced, and his mother had begun working to support the family. Georgie spent his days in a nursery. It seemed that Georgie had only one joy from life—thumb-sucking—and for that, he was not dependent upon anyone but himself. Georgie's mother felt that her marital difficulties could not be related to Georgie's thumb-sucking, because, "We never fought in front of the children." It is not what you say, or what you do not say, but how you say it and what you feel that is important. Although open fighting between parents is to be deplored, the growing and impressionable child immediately senses the existence of fundamental and persistent differences between his parents, even if such differences are not verbalized or acted out. Such parental discords injure the emotional growth of the child.

There are also circumstances in which a child reverts to the behavior of an earlier stage of emotional development (see p. 68). Marcia was brought to the physician's office by an anxious mother. The child, 8 years old, had been progressing in a generally healthy manner until about 6 months earlier when she became very nervous; began to have trouble learning her lessons at school; started fighting with her playmates; had frequent episodes of crying over minor matters; began wetting the bed at night; and started sucking her thumb. The mother was sure that all these complaints were due to Marcia's teacher. Marcia had been assigned to this particular teacher's class 6 months earlier, and, "Marcia doesn't want to go to school in the mornings, Doctor. Wants to stay home. She doesn't even enjoy going out to play with her friends. When she does play with them, she always seems to get into a fight. I can't understand it. She always liked school. Had good grades, and now her grades are terrible. I'm ashamed of her. I don't know what to do. I've talked to her teacher. She says Marcia just won't concentrate on her lessons and doesn't get along with others. Marcia was all right until this grade. I don't know what to do, I'm so nervous myself these days. . . ."

The physician found that Marcia's mother and father were not getting along well together. Marcia, of course, was aware of this situation. The parents had little time for Marcia, who felt neglected and angry. She took out her anger on her playmates and everyone she met. And since Marcia felt unwanted at home, she was afraid to leave home and lose what little love she already had. She also was not sure what might happen at home during her absence. Her mother and father might leave her! Life was no longer fun. Marcia had been happy, however, when she was younger. Therefore, another way of escaping the tension of the current situation was to get away from the unhappy present to the happier past—to the behavior of an earlier phase of her development. Thumb-sucking reappeared. As in other cases of emotional disturbance, thumb-sucking was only one of many symptoms. It was much easier for the mother to blame the teacher than the home situation or herself. The physician often sees teachers blamed by parents for problems that originate in the home.

Another problem is that of Abby who had been an only child until her sister was born. Abby, 4 years old, had not used a bottle for years. When her sister, Susie, was born, Susie received presents from all the adoring relatives, but no one remembered Abby who used to get all the attention and presents. Now, when her father comes home from work, he runs to see Susie and brushes by Abby who was used to kissing her father immediately after his arrival home. Abby has begun to demand a bottle. She is competing with her baby sister for her father's love and attention by behaving like her baby sister.

Any parent is aware of the gratifyingly healthy appetite of the newborn. The child's eating behavior at this stage is a most sensitive indicator of the child's responses to the outside world. The healthy, happy child at this stage eats well. If the emotional relationship and the physical health are sound, it makes no difference whether the child is fed on a strict schedule or by self-demand, breast or bottle. It would be well at this point to review a few basic points of child growth.

The average child weighs 7 pounds at birth. Usually he will have doubled his birth weight at 4 months of age, but it will take him about 8 more months to gain 7 more pounds. Therefore, by 1 year of age, the average child weighs 21 pounds. Then it will take him about one whole year to gain another 7 pounds so that he will weigh an average of 28 pounds at 2 years of age. It is evident that the child's initial rapid gain of weight is not maintained. Although the child continues to gain, of course, he gains less rapidly as he grows older. Even after these known facts are explained, some mothers still will not accept them. If such mothers were correct in their erroneous assumption that the child will continue to gain as rapidly as he did at first, it would mean that the child would double his weight every 4 months. A little simple arithmetic would show that, were this to happen, the child would weigh 448 pounds at 2 years of age! Therefore, since the child is gaining less as he gets older, his appetite also lessens proportionately. This is not to say that the 2-year-old child east less than the 4-month old baby. However, pound for pound of body weight, the 2-year-old does eat less. A noticeable decrease of appetite occurs usually at about 18 to 24 months of age. Parents who are not aware of this natural course of events frequently become alarmed and therefore may try to force, bribe, or coax the child to eat. It is at this stage that feeding problems often first appear.

Mr. and Mrs. H. brought their 6-year-old Clarence to the physician's office. They appeared to be extremely worried as they spoke to the physician. "We need help very much, Doctor. We've taken Clarence all over. He's been examined thoroughly. He's had all the tests, and he's even been put in the hospital for observation. But no one has been able to make Clarence eat. He just won't eat. He never has any appetite. He doesn't eat enough to keep a bird alive." Of course, the child had eaten well until about 2 years of age, but after that the appetite fell off, and troubles had appeared. The mother had tried every possible means, including vitamins, to no avail. Well aware that the mother had excellent advice but, possibly for her own emotional problems, could not accept the explanations, little Clarence was admitted to the hospital for study. The nurses were ordered to offer the child a regular diet for his age 3 times every day, make sure that he had no candy between meals and make no special point about whether he ate or not. He was permitted full play activity. The problem was clarified in part when the distraught nurse phoned the physician saying, "What can we do about Mrs. H.? She insists on staying with Clarence to make sure he eats and has even brought in baskets of fruit and boxes of candy 'to keep up his strength.' " Mrs. H. was, of course, extremely confused, and a simple explanation could not suffice.

Mothers with similar feeding problems usually benefit from a simple explanation. "Doctor, Jane is really much better since I was here 2 weeks ago. We did what you told us. We offered her food at mealtimes. If she wanted it, she took it. If she didn't want to eat, we made no fuss over it."

Byron presented another problem. He was irritable and, as his mother said, "lazy like his father." His short life span of 14 months had been a succession of infections. "I give him his vitamins, Doctor; still he has no resistance; but look at him, look at how fat he is; he looks healthy." Byron was obese, but he did not look healthy. The physician, noting the extreme pallor of the skin, immediately questioned the mother on Byron's eating habits. He found that the mother was feeding Byron only milk. He drank as much as 2½ quarts of milk a day, but he was not offered any solid foods. The mother had tried some solid foods when Byron was 3 months old; he refused, so she had pressed no further. Since milk lacks adequate quantities of iron, Byron was suffering from a very severe anemia, and this was the cause of his pale and pasty appearance and his poor resistance to infections.

Except for the rare cases of true food allergy, the likes and the dislikes that a child has for any particular food are reflections of his parents' tastes. "My David won't look at eggs, and I know they're good for him." "Do you eat eggs, Mrs. S.?" A grimace of extreme distaste, "I can't stand the sight of them! But, Doctor, I tell him they're good for him, and I don't tell him I don't like them." A child senses the parents' feelings in this as in other matters, whether the parent talks of his feelings or not. The father's eating habits also influence the child's likes and dislikes for particular foods, especially in boys who tend to imitate their fathers.

Preschool children often go through phases during which they will either want just a certain food (for example, macaroni and cheese and peanut butter and jelly sandwiches) or resolutely refuse a certain food or group of foods. This is seen often and usually will disappear of its own accord if the parents do not focus undue attention on the problem.

The child quickly senses the great value and interest that the parents place on eating. Therefore, the child can also use eating as a means of getting back at his parents. Thus, food can become a weapon in the frequent conflicts between parent and child that occur in the natural course of growing up. A child who is happy in the knowledge that he is loved and wanted will get over eating problems very quickly. Therefore, the child's eating problems are frequently the parent-child eating problems.

CHAPTER 2

The Bowel Stage

And Love of Self

By the time the child is 1 year old, he has learned to react in many ways to the world around him: he crawls, stands, perhaps already walks; he reaches for and grasps objects, coos, and recognizes familiar persons. In short, the child becomes fun for the proud parents. But as he learns to respond more and more to people and objects around him, society, through the parents and other family members, begins to make demands upon the baby. Shortly after this time (usually by 1½ to 2 years of age) the child begins bowel-training. Later, he must also be bladder-trained. The child must learn to keep himself clean, feed himself, make his wants known and, finally, he must learn to talk. The acquisition of all this new knowledge takes time, and it cannot all be done at once. Consider how difficult it is for adults to learn something new like a foreign language, and one can realize how much the parents and society demand from this small child. But, the child does accomplish his tasks remarkably well. How easily he does this depends upon his intelligence and, even more important, on how much the parents demand of him. They too would rebel if more were asked of them than they can reasonably be expected to do.

Bowel-training may lead to an early conflict between parent and child. It is not too rare for a fond mother to boast that her little baby was bowel-trained at 6 months of age. At that stage it is not the baby who is trained but the mother. She has learned that the baby has a bowel movement after a certain meal or at a certain time of the day; therefore, she places the baby on the toilet at that time. But the baby is not trained. How can one expect the brain to send messages to the bowel when the nerve tracts between the brain and the bowel are not even completely developed until about 2 years of age? It is as if one were to expect a lamp to turn on without first plugging it into the wall socket and connecting the lamp with the source of electricty. Bowel-training involves a complicated process of learning. It requires the capacity to recognize the urge to have a bowel movement, to refrain from having the bowel movement on the spot and to let the mother know that he must move his bowels. Therefore, bowel-training usually cannot be accomplished in a few weeks or even in a month or two.

Many emotional factors are also involved in this process. At this time the baby normally develops a great interest in his own body and its products, particularly the stool. Every parent will remember the expression of satisfaction and even pleasure on the baby's face as he grunts and has a bowel movement. When the child first learns to speak, he calls the mother and proudly points to his bowel movement, "Mommy, look!" The mother turns her head in disgust. Her reaction is understandable to herself but can only be a mystery to the child who is proud of what he has done and has not yet learned the adult point of view.

Like giving up the bottle or the breast, learning to have a bowel movement at a definite time and place is a major step forward in the child's development. The mother in reality confronts the child with the necessity of making another major decision in life. He can gain his mother's love by learning to control elimination as she desires and thus surrendering an early pleasure, or he may feel that his mother's censure is less important to him than the continued pleasure of having a bowel movement wherever and whenever he wishes. If the feelings exchanged between parents and child are healthy, each will love and respect the other's needs, and neither will have the compulsion to use the bowel-training situation as a means of establishing dominance over the other. Each—parent and child—enters this situation from a position of strength. The parents are big and strong, and the child is dependent on them for his needs; but the bowel movements are the child's own and will be passed by him where and when he chooses. Therefore, it is not a question of the parents' "breaking the child in" but of their being patient, understanding and respectful. Sensing these feelings, the child in turn will willingly give up the pleasures from his own body in return for his parents' love. He will learn to get greater pleasure by sharing feelings with people than by depending on his own body. In the process of learning bowel control in this way, the child will also acquire the same healthy love, patience, undestanding and respect for his parents (and other people) that his parents showed him.

During the bowel stage of development, any child shows extreme interest in and gets profound enjoyment from bowel movements and from anything which may remind him of them. The child in the second year of life enjoys having bowel movements, making mud pies, getting smeared with dirt and playing in sand. Giving daily enemas or otherwise directing undue attention to this part or function of his body will increase his awareness of and indelibly impress on his memory interests which are already uppermost in his mind at this time of life. Emotional remnants from this early time may, following such experiences, persist in later life in the form of preoccupation with bowel movements, bowel regularity, enemas, cathartics, odors and cleanliness. Saying that the individual would thus retain some of the interests and enjoyments common to the bowel stage of development does not mean that he or she fails to advance intellectually or in other spheres of emotional development (i.e., sexual). For example, a man and a woman can enjoy marriage and children and be of above average intelligence and still be preoccupied with their own bowel movements and those of their children.

The child who has just become bowel-trained has given up something pleasurable to him in return for his mother's continued acceptance and love; but the need for this early elemental pleasure derived from the body and its products often continues and must be satisfied. Society, as seen through his parents' attitudes and feelings, discourages his soiling himself. Therefore, the child will seek and find substitutes acceptable to society and affording him types of pleasure similar to those which he has had to give up. There is the 2-year-old who makes mud pies and might become the 4-year-old who finger-paints, models clay and likes to get into the dough that his mother is kneading for the apple pie. Some children just "can never stay clean."

The early interest of the young child in his products of elimination may be transferred to collecting stones, seashells and leaves of different shapes and colors. In the older child and adult this early tendency may develop into various hob-bies: collections of coins and stamps, minerals, butterflies, books and jewelry. As the child grows older, the original simple activity becomes a thousandfold more complex, and the original connection with bowel-training becomes com-pletely and forever forgotten. Such substitution of construc-tive and commendable forms of behavior for behavior upon which society will frown is seen in all the various stages of a child's emotional development (see also pp. 4 and 5).

In the face of his great pleasure from soiling, the young child may respond to his parents' excessive demands for clean-liness (stemming from the attitudes of their own parents in this matter) by overcorrection. He will acquire the same val-ues in such matters as his parents. He will be obsessed with the same overwhelming need for cleanliness and for pleasant odors. Overcorrection may occur in many other areas of the child's emotional development throughout life. He may solve the problem posed by a forbidden need or desire by over-correction. Thus, the one who hates might overly protest his love. The one who is envious might overly shout his joy at another's fortune. The individual who is very sensitive about bad odors might chew mints or gum for his breath and use deodorants and perfume to excess.

At this point, it would be well to digress by returning to the very young child and trace the origins of one other important feature of the bowel stage of development. Any mother who has watched her baby grow will remember that during the first few months of life the child was generally perfectly satis-fied with being fed, having his diapers changed and being put back into his crib. Gradually, his interest in the world about him awakened so that by 4 or 5 months of age, the child enjoyed being propped up on pillows so he could view what went on around him. Gradually, as he developed the abilities to crawl, walk and handle objects with some degree of skill, he was able to satisfy this curiosity in the world around him without the help of the adults. "He's always in the way." "He's always into something." "He's full of mischief." Actually, he is only satisfying his curiosity. But, many of his explorations and discoveries are ill-fated. In the process of learning he makes many mistakes and may even injure himself. The accident rate at this age is particularly high.

With this increasing ability to get about by himself and procure what he wants for himself, the child becomes very confident of his own abilities. He slowly masters bowel control, the ability to express himself verbally and the ability to feed himself. He becomes increasingly independent and wants to do everything for himself. With this extreme confidence in his own abilities and with this growing tendency to depend upon himself to get what he wants, the child becomes very self-centered and develops a strong love of self. For example, in a room full of 2-year-olds, there would be much independent activity and little group activity. As the child grows older, his center of interest normally but slowly shifts from himself to other people. The 3-year-old, who is leaving the bowel stage of his development, is much more gregarious.

CHAPTER 3

The First Romance

"Daddy! Daddy! Read me the funnies! You promised last night that you would do it. Come on, daddy! Joanie's daddy does it every Sunday." With his Sunday morning sleep shattered, Mr. Jones broke out into a smile, held little Laurie, gave her a kiss and said, "You are really Daddy's girl. I think you're better than Mommy." Indulgently, Mother left the room to start Sunday breakfast, leaving 5-year-old Laurie snuggled next to Daddy in bed.

Mr. Thomas, who was on vacation, awakened to hear the patter of his 3-year-old daughter's feet along the hallway from her room to his. "Honey," said his wife, "what will we do? Here she comes again. This is the second time now." "Well, I know what I'm going to do. She can't sleep with us. That I know." Mr. Thomas reluctantly but gamely got out of bed, met his daughter at the door, gently but firmly grasped her shoulders, turned her around and said, "Back to your own bed, Honey."

Four-year-old Sue's father always finds her waiting for him as he comes home at night. She is always at the door, ready to grab him around the knees begging to be picked up. In fact, it is very difficult for him to kiss his wife. "No, Daddy, don't kiss Mommy. Kiss me first."

By 3 years of age, both Edith and her twin brother, Tommy, sit at their own small table and feed themselves with little help from the grownups. They can even dress themselves, if their mother helps them with the buttons and the shoelaces. They also no longer soil or wet themselves and usually remain dry through the night. With these necessary tasks in the proc-

ess of growing up accomplished, they now turn to other interests. Edith wonders why Mommy and Daddy sleep in their
own room and why she must sleep apart. Can't she sleep with
Daddy too? After all, she is a girl just like Mommy. "When
I grow up, I want to be as pretty as you, Mommy. Then I
can marry Daddy." Tommy asks, "Mommy, will you wait for
me until I grow up and marry you, just like Daddy?" Ador-
ingly, his mother promises, but asks, "But, what will we do
with Daddy?" "Oh, he's always busy at the office anyway,
Mommy; he's never home." However, later in the day, Tommy
says, "When I grow up, I want to be a lawyer, just like Daddy.
Gee, Daddy can do anything!"

Mrs. W.'s physician asked, "Even though your husband is
often away on sales trips, why do you sleep with your 5-year-
old son?" "But, Doctor, aren't you supposed to love your son?
All my friends sleep with their children! After all, what can
there be between a mother and her 5-year-old son? I dress
in front of him; take showers with him; and I let him come
into bed with me. I suppose you're going to say that isn't
good for him. I can see nothing wrong in it."

"Let me say this, Mrs. W. This problem is very easy to
understand on one hand but difficult to grasp on the other.
If you watch your children and your neighbor's children, you
might see how some of this behavior which you say is so innocent can only badly confuse and disturb your child. You
see, extending from 3 until about age 6, little boys and little
girls, in their feelings for their parents, develop attitudes
which will guide them through all their later lives in their
relationships with other people of the same and opposite sex.
These early blueprint feelings are the keystones for all their
later feelings and behavior, be it their choice of husband or
wife or how they get along with other people, their employer,
friends and wife or husband. These feelings depend on the
way you treat your child and the way you feel toward your
child.

"Little boys at this period, from 3 to 6 years of age, begin
to turn their interests from their own bodies to other people.
And the people in whom they are most interested are those
individuals who have been closest to them and have done the

most to care for their needs in the past—the parents. Boys begin to notice that they are built differently from little girls. This might have come from seeing their sister, little friends, a new baby, or the mother. You have, I'm sure, seen manifestations of this new curiosity in your own child. It is at this age that little boys and girls may examine each other's bodies; show extreme interest when the mother changes the diapers or bathes the new baby; or first play 'doctor' or 'house'.

"With this new curiosity, the boy turns to the most important person of the opposite sex in his life, his mother. He has always been close to his mother, closer than to his father, but only because she has done more to take care of him than his father. She has fed him, bathed him, kept him warm, dressed him, cuddled him, guided his first steps, taught him his first words and, all through her love for him, she has taught him how to control elimination. He has been close to her, because he has been greatly dependent upon her. But now, at about 3 to 4 years of age, he first becomes aware that she is built differently and must be treated differently from his father and himself. He knows that men and women go together, and he notices that his father, who is built like himself, is close to his mother, closer than even the boy can be and possibly in a different way. Much goes on between them from which he is excluded, which he does not even understand. The little boy wonders why he cannot be as close to his mother as is the father. He begins to wish that he could be grown up like the father and thus also become as close to the mother as is the father. The little boy cherishes the secret hope that he may grow up to have his mother for himself. He may even ask the mother to wait for him.

"But, this same little boy also has always been close to his father and has depended upon his father. Recognizing that he is built like the father, the little boy nurtures the fond hope that some day he can be just like his father who is so much bigger and stronger than he is and is so loved and respected by Mommy. To achieve this goal, the little boy will imitate his father. He may ape his father's walk or manner of speech, work by his father's side in the tool shed or garden, or he may say he wants to go into the same vocation as his father. He may even want to excel his father.

"The little boy is confronted with an upsetting dilemma. In wanting his mother for himself, he must compete with his father who is so much bigger and stronger. The little boy loves him, respects and depends upon him, but in spite of this love and respect, the boy often feels angry toward his father when he sees the father close to the mother in a way that he cannot be.

"This dilemma is resolved by the attitudes of the mother and the father in dealing with their child. For example, the mother should realize that this is a natural and healthy stage through which her son is passing and that, through the feelings exchanged between them, he will establish a blueprint for all his later successes and failures with the opposite sex. The mother should realistically accept her son's affections in a mother-son fashion. She should be honest with him in her feelings for him. She should do everything possible to sustain a healthy son-mother affection for herself rather than confuse his growing up by giving her son any reason to believe that his yearnings to supplant his father and have his mother all for himself may some day come true. It is unfair for the mother to treat her son in any manner suggestive of a husband-wife relationship. This would only confuse the little boy and cruelly distort the little boy's future feelings and behavior toward his mother and the opposite sex. For example, at this stage of earliest manhood, the mother should realize that taking a shower with her son will not enhance his emotional growth any more than sleeping with him.

"When the boy grows up, he may not be able to sever these unnatural ties to his mother. He may be unable to enter into a mature husband-wife relationship with another woman, and he may always search for his mother or someone who reminds him of her. He will never be satisfied. Never having had a comfortable and healthy parent-child relationship as a child, he may never be able to develop a comfortable parent-child relationship as a father. These unnatural activities can be very frustrating to a little boy, because he is permitted, even encouraged, to do certain things with his mother. Then without

apparent reason to the boy, it is stopped. Seeing mother undress only serves to overstimulate the healthy curiosity of this
stage of development in an unnatural and unhealthy way.
Such behavior causes the boy to assume a role too much like
that of his father who lives in the same room with his mother
and undresses with her. The reverse situation in the father-
girl relationship has similar implications."

Similarly, when a mother breast-feeds the baby, little is
gained for the older child to watch. This, like undressing in
front of the older child, might only serve to confuse him.
Witnessing such an intimate situation in which the baby is
sustained solely via the breast can only serve to let Johnny
feel, "Why is it that the baby can be so close to Mommy and
get this when I can't." This situation mobilizes all the still
recent longings and feelings in the young child who is just
beginning to assume some degree of independence. The
mother may say, "Johnny never said a word when I breast-fed
Lucy." Was it that Johnny did not care or was it really that
Johnny was flustered and could not discuss the subject, especially since he was getting older and knew that grownups had
strange ideas and values attached to this part of the body?
Any parental feelings or behavior which kept reminding the
child of his recent complete dependence and discourage or
thwart his budding independence will keep the child young
and mar his character development. Such feelings and behavior, by their effects, can only be considered unfriendly.

An extreme example of this type with, however, definite
overtones of a highly disturbed mother-son relationship was
that of Mrs. L. and her son, David. While preparing to
breast-feed the baby, she teasingly turned to her 5-year-old
son, "Come on, David, it's time for your breakfast." Such a
taunting statement is very cruel and only serves to imprint
on a young and impressionable mind an unnatural alliance
of sex and hate.

Mrs. W.'s physician continued:

"Unfortunately, the other side of the coin is perhaps even
more important and almost invariably never noticed. For
example, Mrs. W., you tell me your husband is a salesman,
always away during the week, and, for that reason, you take

your son to bed with you at night. Would it not seem to you that this business with your son perhaps gratifies your own understandable needs rather than his? From what you understand of his needs at this crucial time and from what you've said of your sleeping with him, it would seem to be a very unusual way of showing mother-son love.

"Now, we have so far talked of you, Mrs. W., and this certainly does not mean it is all a mother's responsibility at this period. For example, is your husband bored and tired when he comes home from work? Does he sit down and read the paper and watch TV while ignoring his son? Is he patient and understanding when his son plays baseball as a 5-year-old might instead of playing like a Babe Ruth? When he plays with his young son, does he do so for the pleasure that he and his son can get out of it together or does your husband do so only to show off his own admittedly superior strength and skill in definite competition with his son? The son will recognize such actions for what they really are—confusing and unfriendly. Some fathers are keenly aware of their son's strivings in relation to the mother and frankly resent it. Does one parent unwittingly use the young son (or daughter) as the most readily available means by which the parent may show his jealousy and anger at the other parent? The young innocent child is totally unable to defend himself from being so used. If the father is comfortable in his feelings toward his son, he will be able to put himself in his son's shoes, and he will be able to accept with a friendly smile and without rancor his son's natural competition with him for his wife."

It may also be stated at this time that a boy is not helped if his father is a very passive "jellyfish" while his mother "wears the pants" in the family. Little Donald G.'s mother is president of several school and social organizations in town. She was very successful in business before marriage and had more formal education than her husband. She is now busy organizing the women of her town into a solid slate for the next election. Donald's father works in a bank all day and returns home at 5:00 P.M. in time to cook and serve the evening meal. Mrs. G. has him handle the family wash and the housecleaning. She even boasts that her son makes his own bed every

morning. It has been said by Mr. G.'s associates that he has
not made his Maine fishing trip in 15 years of marriage because his wife was always too ill or had "allergies" at the
time for which the trip was planned. Mrs. G. boasts to her
friends about her husband, "If he weren't so good, I'd divorce
him in a minute!" Like any other boy, Donald imitates his
father. However, in this situation, he is imitating an easy-
going, passive and effeminate individual.

Neither the husband nor the wife should take advantage
(merely to solve their own problems and to gratify their own
warped desires) of these natural feelings of competition and
love which the child shows at this stage of emotional development. If the parents manage these problems in a healthy
manner, the child will pass successfully through the first romance stage strengthened by his parents' love and their genuine respect for him rather than weakened and confused by
being made the scapegoat for his parents' own problems. In
this way, the parents will have helped him lay strong and
healthy foundations for his future relations with his own and
opposite sex.

The same can be said for the little girl and her curiosity
about and closeness to the father. She might wonder why she
is not made like her brother, or she might wonder if something happened to make her different. This curiosity, as in
the boy, may be unnecessarily stimulated by unhealthy situations in the home. For instance little 5-year-old Wanda is not
helped by her Sunday morning showers with her father or his
yielding to her importunities to play hobbyhorse as a reward.
Nor is it healthy, even though it is a warm day, for 14-year-
old Diane to parade around the living room in her brassière
and panties. Her mother proudly explains, "This doesn't go
on in front of everybody . . . just with the immediate family
and friends." This same mother also added confidentially,
"Isn't Diane cute; she's only 14, yet walks just like a chorus
girl!"

Lynn's father was very close to her. Even when she was in
her 'teens he would hold her on his lap, snuggle her to him
and whisper that he loved her. She had always been "Daddy's
girl" and always was seen with her father. He enjoyed helping

her bathe and washing her back (even until her 'teens), and there was a complete open-door policy in this "modern" home where "the old fogey notions" were not allowed. As in bathing, there was neither modesty nor privacy in the family dressing habits and conversations. However, the physician wondered how much such behavior represented the father's love for Lynn and how much it represented a distortion of his own needs. Lynn's father and mother did not get along well together. They frequently argued and often would not speak to each other for hours or even days at a time. For as long as Lynn could remember, her parents had separate bedrooms, ostensibly because her father liked a cold room, and her mother said he snored so loudly that she could not sleep. From watching her parents, Lynn had many distorted ideas about marriage and the roles of a father, a mother and a daughter. As a result of her unnatural closeness to her father, Lynn had reason to believe that she was truly her Daddy's girl friend. But Mother still lurked in the shadows. Lynn felt that her Daddy wanted her very much. As she grew older, his attentions posed serious problems. Instead of advancing to later stages of emotional development, Lynn remained fixed emotionally at the first romance stage. She continued to compete with her mother for her father's affections long after such competition should have been resolved. This competition brought with it heavy burdens of guilt toward her mother. But these specific feelings, in time, extended to affect her attitudes in general. Her feelings of competition with her mother slowly extended so she felt that she had to compete with all women in all fields. She never could be friendly or comfortable with members of her own sex. Her feelings toward her father extended to affect her attitudes toward all men. She could not give of herself fully to any man without a similar feeling of guilt. Her later conceptions of love were limited almost solely to the early physical expressions and whisperings shared with her father. She could only function at the immature level of the first romance stage of emotional development.

The physician followed Lynn for many years. She grew up to be a very intelligent and beautiful woman. She had many boy friends and always was the most courted "belle of the ball." After many heart-breaking false starts, Lynn married. Knowing how unhappy her father and mother had been together, she had been afraid of marriage and finally had entered it determined to make it succeed. In this, too, she was doomed to unhappiness because of the unhealthy feelings toward men which had become indelibly impressed on her character. She had expensive clothes, a home, a maid, an automobile and everything material that a young woman might want, but she was dissatisfied and unhappy. She envied her friends who were happily married. She knew that life must have more to offer, but that for some reason it had passed her by. And she never knew why. Her life became a constant search for this elusive goal: parties, travel, repeated divorces and marriages. . . .

The little girl must contend with problems similar to that of the little boy. She tends to imitate the mother whom she loves and respects and upon whom she is dependent; she also tends to compete with her mother for the attention and affection of her father. The outcome of this early clash of feelings sets the stage for her later feelings and modes of behavior with people of the same and also the opposite sex.

It is very important for the parents to know that their little girl or boy will acquire, without either parent's or child's necessarily being aware of what is happening, all the feelings and the attitudes of the parents. The child will acquire the same ideals and prejudices and the same virtues and vices of the parents. In many subtle ways the child will keenly sense the underlying feelings, attitudes and values, the deep loves, hates, needs and forbidden wishes that motivate the parents. And the child will make these feelings his own. These strong undercurrents which determine the parents' own feelings and behavior despite any verbal professions to the contrary, will similarly determine the feelings and the behavior of the child. The child learns what the parent actually feels and not what the parent may only profess to feel when the parents' feelings and what he professes to feel are different. The parent and the child may not even be aware of this divergence.

"Where do babies come from, Mommy?" This natural question often embarrasses the parent or sends her scurrying to the nearest bookshelf for information on what to say. If the mother is flustered and tries to pass it off, the child senses that this is a taboo subject and will not touch on it again. Thus, parents often say, "My child has never asked me that, Doctor. I guess she's not interested." It is less a matter of the child's disinterest and more a matter of the parental attitude toward the subject. The reason most parents are embarrassed is that they themselves have been brought up to look at the entire subject as one that is just not discussed. "Well, Doctor, what do I say and how much—and when do I say it?" If the parents are comfortable in discussing this subject, the child will sense the parents' poise and relaxed attitude. At that point the child wants a simple direct answer to the question she asks. She is not interested in an elaborate explanation nor does she need or expect one. "Where do little babies come from, Mommy?" The answer might be, "From inside Mommy's body." If the child has any further questions at that time, she will ask them, and the answer should be just as direct and simple. But most often no further questions will be asked then.

After mulling over this problem for days to weeks or months the child usually asks, "How do babies get into Mommy's body?" Again the answer should be simple and direct, "By a seed planted there by the Daddy." How do they get out? "Through a birth canal that Mommies have." It is seldom that more questions are asked, but the same literal answers should be given. It is unnecessary and definitely inadvisable to demonstrate the anatomy to the child.

Bobby H., aged 4½, was coasting along quite well until his baby sister was born. Mother had prepared Bobby for his sister's arrival by telling him that the family would soon have a new baby in the house and that, since Bobby was such a big boy, Mommy would need his help. Realizing that a 4½-year-old cannot remember things for long periods of time, his mother told him this only shortly before the expected time of birth, and a few times thereafter in response to his questions about her "big tummy." At this time, Bobby was bowel-trained; remained dry during the daytime; only rarely wet the bed at night; fed himself; and had not been on the bottle for about 2½ years. Mrs. H. called the physician 10 days after she returned home from the hospital with Irene. "Doctor, what can I do? Bobby keeps pestering me all the time. He wants attention, and I don't have all that time. He has started soiling and wetting himself again. And now he even wants a bottle. The other day he said he wanted to hold the baby, and he squeezed so tightly I was afraid he would hurt her. This morning he hit the baby with his Teddy bear. I know he's jealous of the baby. What can I do?"

Actually, Bobby's reaction to his sister's arrival home was predictable. Until this time he had been the only child in the home; his little world had revolved about him. When Daddy came home at night, he used to speak to Bobby first. Mother always had been with Bobby. When the grandparents visited the house, they had looked for Bobby first and brought presents for him and only for him. Things were different after the baby arrived. Daddy, on coming home at night would make a bee-line for the nursery to look at her. Now, when the grandparents visited, they brought presents only for the baby and virtually ignored Bobby. Seemingly, his mother was always busy feeding or dressing the baby, changing her diapers—or just admiring her. It was natural for Bobby to feel that the baby had displaced him in the affections of his parents. What other reaction could be expected from Bobby than jealousy and anger toward the new baby? Perhaps, if he were to act like a baby, exactly like Irene, he could be loved again. Furthermore, Bobby's babyhood had been a happy and comfortable time, and there would be a tendency for him, without his even being aware of it, to revert in his behavior to some period in his past life when things were less complicated and more pleasant. This reaction is common to many children and adults when faced with an intolerable current situation. It is not difficult to see why Bobby reverted to soiling, wetting, desire for a bottle, thumb-sucking and constant requests to be picked up. A certain degree of temporary return to babylike behavior by the older child after the arrival of a new baby is so often seen as to be no cause for concern.

The question, therefore, is often not "Will he act like a baby?" but rather, "Doctor, what can I do about it?"

"The main thing is to show Bobby that you love him. 'Bobby, I know that you feel that since we have to spend so much time in caring for the baby, we love the baby more than we do you. That is not true. We love you and the baby the same. It is only that since the baby is so small, she cannot take care of herself, just the way you could not take care of yourself when you were small. Now, you are big and can take care of yourself and help Mommy. But we still love you.' More important than what you say is how you say it. You can tell a child many things. You can say 'I love you' in such a firm, cold and nasty manner as to frighten the child. You can also say 'I love you' in such a gentle, sincere way that the child will sense immediately that you do love him. Or, you can say nothing and just love him!"

The physician continued, "It is also important that you and your husband show Bobby your love in many little ways. While the baby is asleep, Mother, take time to read to Bobby; play with him; show him attention. There is no reason why his father cannot first speak to Bobby when he arrives home at night before going to see the baby. Father can spend time in the backyard or the living room with Bobby before bedtime. Why can't the grandparents and all visitors bring a present for Bobby whenever they bring a gift for the baby? If the doting grandparents do bring a gift only for Irene, it would be wise for you, the parents, to have small toys or knickknacks that can be given to Bobby at the same time. You, the mother, might have Bobby help with the care of the baby when he can. You might have him carry diapers for you. But do not make an issue of this. Be guided by Bobby's own feelings. When you said you were afraid that Bobby squeezed the baby too hard even though he was only wanting to show the baby love, you may have been correct. He probably did squeeze too hard. In the situation that you described, Bobby would understandably feel angry with Irene, his apparently successful competitor for your affections. It is ironic. Bobby has learned many things. The baby is helpless, squalling, spitting, soiling and even somewhat smelly. In spite of all this,

Irene gets the presents and the attention while Bobby feels frozen out of the family circle. Show Bobby that you still love him—as I know you do. If you do this, Bobby will gradually get over this babylike behavior, since the need to behave in that manner will no longer exist. Above all, do not make fun of him and do not punish him for the babylike behavior. If you do, it will only prove to him that he is right in fearing that he has lost your affection. If you react correctly to the situation, these symptoms (which, I repeat, many children show to varying degrees with the arrival of a new baby) will gradually disappear. If you, the mother (and the father), react poorly to this situation, these symptoms, which should last only a short time, may persist, become fixed to some degree and may influence Bobby's future feelings toward the baby, toward you, the parents, and toward other significant people with whom he may feel to be in competition in later life. This is the first time that a brother and a sister compete for their parents' affection. Such competition will recur innumerable times in the future. Whether this competition is resolved with or without ill effects is determined by the parents' attitude toward their children—which in turn is dependent upon the feelings and the experiences from the parents' own childhoods."

The telephone rings. "This is Mrs. M. I need help. This morning I caught Eloise . . . she's 4 years old, you know . . . she was being undressed by a 5-year-old neighbor boy. I talked to his mother, and she is just as upset and surprised as I am. We don't know what to do or where to turn. Could he hurt her? Can you examine and see? I want to come down to the office with Eloise and Johnny's mother right now. What should I do? I didn't think she'd ever do this to me!"

During the 3- to 6-years-of-age period children are becoming more aware of their bodies and of the differences between the sexes. They are curious and naturally look into the matter. This mother's extreme apprehensiveness and readiness to assume that Eloise was hurt might make the physician wonder about the mother's own problems in this emotional sphere. The fears of such a mother might be a symptom of her own insecure feelings toward men; she might fear that men only hurt women. Her physician knows that Eloise's mother also has fears concerning her older son; she fears that he may catch some dread infection, get run over or get into trouble with girls.

Returning now to the situation that brings Mrs. M. to the office with Eloise, it is necessary for the physician to explain to Mrs. M. the child's natural curiosity at this age. It is not an abnormality and should shortly disappear of its own accord. The child should be told that the grownups know that she is curious, and they understand how she feels, but boys and girls should not undress together, because it is not how grownups should act.

Since society has certain rules of conduct, these rules should be applied to the child as well as to the adult, and the child will accept this explanation if it is presented in this way. The adult should avoid undue attention to the problem or any threats of dire punishment. Such exaggerated behavior could only communicate to the child the parents' own warped emotions and distorted values toward the subject of sex. "But, Doctor, if I don't punish her and emphasize how terrible that is, I'm afraid she might do it again!" If the parents' feelings toward the opposite sex are healthy, they will accept the situation for what it is—the expression of the normal curiosity seen in children at this stage of development. Such healthy parents, whose own feelings toward the opposite sex are appropriate, will not fear that such a situation will become the prelude to later elaborations and repetitions. Such parents need not fear that their child will get into any trouble because of sex, because their child will already have acquired the same healthy attitudes and will continue to develop in the same healthy manner.

It is good for the parents to set limits to the child's activity and for the child to know definitely from the parents' feelings and behavior what he can and cannot do. This advice is applicable throughout the child's growing years and adolescence.

At approximately 6 years of age, Tom and Diane have good-naturedly accepted the fact that growing up means that the love they have for their mother and father and the love their parents have for them is different from the way their parents love each other. Partially as a result of this realization that

Tom cannot have Mommy for himself nor Diane, Daddy, they claim that they really never wanted them anyway. Each seeks out companions of his or her own sex. As a result, from about 6 years of age until puberty, boys commonly organize into clubs of their own and girls play together. Each group practically denies the existence of the other. That this is really not the case, though, is well shown by the way boys and girls often tease each other and by the way boys pull girls' pigtails and groups of boys playfully interfere with girls' activities. "Mommy, make Tom and Sam leave us alone!" "We're not doing anything, Mother, we're just looking." In fact, little boys commonly feel very fond of little girls (and, similarly, the girls are fond of the boys) but are very embarrassed about admitting it. In imitation of their parents and with genuine affection, they occasionally like to kiss and hug little girls of their choice. It is best for parents to accept such actions at their face value. They are entirely appropriate, and such tender feelings should be recognized.

The parent should not offer any comments which ridicule the child or might instill highly suggestive insinuations that the child will understand poorly—ideas that would be applicable only to adult situations. As Mrs. Brown walked over to the house with her daughter, Dickie jumped off the swing, ran to little Cynthia and kissed her on the cheek. Mrs. Brown laughed and said, trying to impress Dickie's mother and father with her own sophistication, "These modern kids are really precocious, aren't they? No telling what they'll do when they grow up." Another mother's reaction in a similar situation was, "We let our children do what they like; there are no secrets in our house." Mrs. V. gushed, "Francis, you're just like your father. He always had a weakness for pretty girls, and from the looks of his new secretary, he hasn't lost his touch. But, boys will be boys."

"These modern kids are really precocious, aren't they? No telling what they'll do when they grow up." Every good salesman knows that a potential customer may be influenced by repeated exposure to the enthusiasm of the salesman for his own product. The salesman must believe in his own product to sell it. Mere Mumbo-Jumbo sales talk without the salesman himself being firmly convinced of the value of his own product will not sell. Everybody will also agree that anyone intimately and sufficiently long exposed to a contagious disease has a good chance of getting the same disease. Therefore, quarantines, various isolation procedures, sterilization and the washing of hands are all accepted by nonmedical people without question. Yet, many people will often doubt the physician's suggestion that certain ideas and feelings, repeated often enough, may inoculate the patient with an emotion which may be either healthy or unhealthy. These ideas and feelings may be presented directly by words and actions, by verbal insinuation, or more deviously but as effectively, by tone of voice, facial expression, half smiles and failures to comment when indicated. The parent may even verbally forbid repetition of the act, but may show rapt and consuming interest when the child relates his story. Or, the parent may misinterpret and give a completely distorted meaning to a child's innocent remark or behavior. Then the child will make this distortion his own as in the above example.

"These modern kids are really precocious, aren't they? No telling what they'll do when they grow up." Why should a parent with a sound conscience insinuate that the child will show unhealthy interests and reactions when he grows up? Should there be any doubt that the child will be anything but a happy, stable, emotionally healthy, law-abiding citizen? If the child has been raised properly, emotionally and morally as well as physically (diet, vitamins, immunizations, and so forth), these things will take care of themselves. If such doubts are expressed often enough and if the parent sincerely feels that such doubts exist, it serves only to inoculate the child with a sick emotion. The effects of such inoculation can be more far-reaching and permanent than the effects of exposure to the germs of many serious diseases. With modern medicines many infectious diseases respond readily and completely to treatment. On the other hand, repeated or prolonged exposure to a sick emotion often leads to an emotionally and morally sick individual who will find it extremely difficult to make any healthy and happy adjustment to life.

Such a person's symptoms of emotional illness may masquerade or actually be manifested as a physical illness. People feel and act as they do because of their ability to perceive and judge what is going on around them and because of their memories of past feelings and experiences. These abilities to perceive, judge and remember are functions of the brain. Everybody knows that nerve fibers go from the brain to every organ and tissue of the body. Any disturbance of the brain, physical or emotional or a combination of the two, may affect the function of the brain, and, secondarily, the ability of other organs and tissues to perform their tasks. For instance, some illnesses which are often related to emotional factors are stomach ulcers, asthma, headaches, itching, nervous indigestion, chronic ulcerative colitis, high blood pressure, fatigue and heart palpitations.

The physician can question the parents directly, and from their description of and reactions to specific situations in their lives he can determine fairly accurately their emotional make-up. With this information frequently he can predict how these people will react in different situations that may arise. However, special technics must be used to determine the emotional make-up of the child.

It is a well-recognized fact that the child (and the adult) expresses his feelings through his play and dreams. These are two methods by which the physician can often solve the mystery of how the child really feels and why he acts as he does. The physician participates in the child's games but lets the child direct their course.

For example, the child may identify several dolls with the members of his own household. By letting the child determine what the dolls will do and what will happen to the dolls in play, the physician can determine how the child feels toward the other members of his family and how the child believes that the other members of his family feel toward each other and toward him. Instead of dolls, the child may have a family of toy animals which, however, behave like their human counterparts. The kinds of toys that the child chooses of his own free will represent the feelings that he has in relation to significant people in his life. These feelings interact with his current stage of emotional development, his past experiences and his hopes and fears concerning the future. The little girl may always want to play with soldiers. The little boy may tenderly feed a baby doll with a toy bottle of milk. The little boy may repeatedly shoot a toy gun at every male animal in sight. The little boy may want to place every block so perfectly in position that he never can complete his toy house. The little girl may repeatedly have the mother doll and the father doll getting hurt in toy automobile crashes. All these children are telling the physician, in their own way, how they really feel, although they may be seldom if ever aware of the relationships of their play and dreams to the real life situations.

By playing the game of "let's pretend" with the child, the physician can get further information. In addition to playing games, the child can be asked to make up stories about specific pictures that the physician shows him. The child might draw pictures which he explains to the physician with stories. Or, the child may play "telephone" with the physician. Each— child and physician—takes the part of a definite member of the child's family (or someone else who is important to the child); the child, of course, is asked to supply the thoughts and the words for both sides of the conversation.

There are other play methods used, but from the examples given it can be seen how the physician can obtain a good insight into the family situation, as the child sees it, and the child's attitudes toward the various members of his family.

One of nature's safety valves in dealing with feelings is dreams. They can express wishes which are frequently un- attainable in everyday life or, more to the point, wishes which are forbidden. Because of the frequently upsetting content of these wishes, they often cannot even be admitted, much less fulfilled, in the everyday life of wakefulness. Nature may pro- tect the individual by permitting him to fulfill these wishes in the dream state. Dreams disguise what would otherwise be upsetting by permitting the individual to do in dreams what he cannot do in his everyday life. Through dreams the emotional tension of these unfulfilled wishes is relieved. By understanding the patient's dreams, the physician can become aware of these feelings and desires which the patient not only hides from the world but also, often, from himself. The physician does not attempt to determine the meaning of any one dream on the basis of that dream alone. And he does not attempt to determine the meaning of even a recurrent dream without thoroughly knowing the emotional and physical background of his patient. This point should be emphasized since the contrary opinion is too often presented to the nonmedical public by many self-styled but naive and misinformed experts. Recurrent dreams are, of course, more significant than isolated ones. "But, Doctor, you say that a dream can be disguised; how can you tell what lies beneath the disguise?" The physician who has studied the dream content of many patients, disguised or otherwise, can determine the meaning when he understands the patient well.

From what has been said about dreams, the recurrent nightmare strongly suggests that the child is having great emotional difficulties. As in every other kind of dream, the nightmare can be understood only by the physician who completely knows the child, his background and his environment.

CHAPTER 4

Becoming a Young Man
or a Young Woman

Marilyn, aged 11, has learned from her friends that at about this time her body will change, and she will enter womanhood. For instance, her friends have told her that her breasts will enlarge, and hair will appear under her arms and on the sexual parts of her body. However, the most mysterious thing is the appearance of monthly bleeding. Once, a few years before, she had seen a box of sanitary napkins and had asked her mother about them. Her mother, without embarrassment and without attempting a lengthy explanation at that time, said that when a girl grows up, she bleeds from below each month. This, she was told, was a sign of healthy growing up, and the mother did not insinuate that there was any uncleanliness, curse, or cause for shame in menstruation. Through the years, Marilyn's mother honestly answered her daughter's questions about the other manifestations of womanhood. Fortunately, Marilyn had not been forced to rely solely upon the misinformation of her friends. Too many girls are forced by false maternal modesty and ignorance to learn about womanhood from this storehouse of old wives' tales and superstitions. Therefore Marilyn looked forward to adolescence and the appearance of womanhood as another phase in growing up.

Enlargement of the breasts is the earliest visible evidence of sexual development in the girl. In most girls, by 10 to 11 years of age, the small nipples of childhood become raised, and the breasts then begin to increase in size. The next evidence of sexual development is the appearance of hair on the sexual areas. At about this same time the bones of the hips will widen, hair will then appear under the arms and, finally, menstrual periods will begin. These visible surface changes are related to the chemical and hormonal changes within the body. Usually a girl will be able to conceive and bear children within approximately a year of the first period, which appears in the average girl at 13½ years of age. With the completion of all these changes, the girl becomes a woman so far as nature is concerned.

But the girl's emotional growth continues beyond this period throughout life. The emotional attitudes and values of the girl during this period are related, it is true, to the physical signs of womanhood, but these emotional attitudes and values are even more dependent upon the emotional attitudes and values of her parents, the individuals who have the greatest influence upon a child's developing personality.

Janet presented an extreme example of the questionable relationship between hormones and a child's developing personality on the one hand and the more definite relationship between parental attitudes and the child's developing personality on the other. She was seen by the physician at 15 years of age, because her periods had not yet appeared. Janet, like her friends, was a happy, well-adjusted adolescent with all the budding interest in boys and increasing attention to her personal appearance that is generally seen in girls her age. However, the physician's examination revealed that Janet should have been named John since "she" really had testicles and a known congenital defect of the external male organs that made them superficially resemble those of a female. However, "she" had the normal amounts of male hormone seen in a 15-year-old boy. But, interestingly enough, during the physician's study of Janet's emotions, it was fully confirmed that "Janet" had all the feelings and values of a healthy girl "her" age. It was apparent that in "her" case, the influence of the male hormones upon "her" personality was less significant than the way "she" was brought up by her parents. Janet had been brought up like a girl, thought like a girl and acted like a girl because her parents had believed that she indeed was a girl.

This is an extreme and rare case which emphasizes the importance of feelings rather than hormones.

The complaint that a daughter's periods have not yet appeared by the time the mother believes they should have done so is heard frequently in the physician's office. It is true that rare conditions such as that of Janet may account for this complaint. However, in the overwhelming majority of cases, this complaint is based on the mother's lack of knowledge of what is really normal. In medicine in general, there is always a wide range of normal. No two people are exactly alike. When the physician states the ages at which the various manifestations of approaching womanhood appear, he really means the average ages. For instance, when he stated that the average age at which menstruation first appears is 13½ years, he implied that menstruation may normally appear several years earlier or later. The same general advice applies to the time of appearance of breast enlargement, body hair and every other change in the growing child.

Laura had a problem. All her girl friends wore brassières and had the general body configuration of young women. Laura had not yet changed, and she keenly sensed the humiliating comparison that some of the boys made between her and her girl friends. The physician who examined Laura found her to be normal and healthy. He explained that there is a wide range of normal, and that some girls develop later than others.

Although none of the women in Laura's family were noted for their figures, the physician knew that they were all good mothers and homemakers. He knew that Laura's father and mother were happy, well-adjusted parents who would support their daughter through her growing-up period. Given the correct understanding and support by her father and mother by genuine feeling rather than by empty words and vain hopes, Laura had a better chance to achieve a truly full and happy life as a woman and mother than some of her friends who had better figures but a disturbed home life. The physician had cared for Laura since her birth, and he knew that she was basically quite sure of herself as a budding woman. The first romance period of development had been well handled by her parents.

In contrast with Laura, the physician thought of another patient, Shirley, whom he had first seen many years earlier when she was a highly disturbed 15-year-old adolescent. She always had been a physically attractive girl and now she had developed into a very beautiful woman. Shirley had been a "cute little tomboy" who missed many days of school due to severe pain during her monthly periods and frequent incapacitating headaches. Her parents never had been able to manage her. Despite all their pleas and commands, she continued to go to wild parties and to remain out until the early hours of the morning. It had been an open secret that Shirley had seen a man much older than herself off and on through the years. She flaunted her beauty and had the deserved reputation of being a coquette. She had no close friends of her own sex and lamented the fact that she was a girl and that boys had all the advantages. Despite the Hollywoodlike glamor that her teen-age friends attached to her "affair," and the superficial appearance of maturity, sophistication and happiness, Shirley was really very immature and unhappy.

Her obvious troubles with men and her difficulty in accepting her own role emotionally as a woman led to many disappointments in love. Countless courses of hormone treatments and repeated surgery never relieved her many physical complaints, which centered around her internal sex organs. The various treatments changed the nature of her complaints but never made her free of complaints. The physician felt that Shirley's early experiences with her father were responsible for her later inability to establish a mature relationship with any man. The physician knew that Shirley's parents never had been able to adjust to each other as husband and wife. The father always had been very close to Shirley. He had helped bathe Shirley until she was 11 years old. This unnaturally close physical contact extended to other activities: tucking Shirley into bed at night until well into her 'teens; napping together; bursting into each other's room while the other was known to be dressing; and the frequent kissing, cuddling and hugging of father and daughter. The father always commented on how pretty Shirley was and how beautiful clothes looked on her. As Shirley entered adolescence, the father began to compliment her on her figure and always wondered aloud how the boys could ever resist her. It was only in these ways that the father showed any interest in his daughter. In all the healthy spheres of a father-daughter relationship, he showed no interest whatever. He cared not at all about her friends, progress in school and everyday successes and failures. Shirley could not turn to him for any genuine support and guidance in dealing with the many problems of her childhood. The physician knew that the father's relationship with Shirley was based not on his "great love" for his daughter (as the father honestly believed and protested) but rather on the father's own sick needs. By such behavior, the father encouraged Shirley's natural feelings of competition with her mother for her father's affection during the first romance stage. He held tantalizingly before his daughter the prospect of what could never be—Shirley's succeeding in her competition with her mother to win her father all for herself. And, by such behavior, he kept her functioning at this stage of development long after she should have progressed beyond it. These early unresolved feelings were ignited further as she entered adolescence and new and stronger longings appeared. In this way, the early attitudes remained to influence her feelings and behavior toward men and women throughout life.

Shirley's early experiences with her father made impossible a mature relationship with any man in later life. Her concept of love with men was derived from her early experiences with her father. Love meant the same superficial expressions unaccompanied by any genuine feelings. Her father's tantalizing behavior toward her was repeated in her coquettish behavior toward men. She became the coquette who, knowing nothing else, never could really give of herself.

Shirley felt tense and uncomfortable in the presence of women as she had with her mother. As a result of the prolonged unresolved competition with her mother, Shirley always had felt angry and therefore guilty toward her. These early feelings of guilt and anger and the need to compete became indelibly stamped on Shirley's character and influenced all her later feelings and behavior toward her mother and all women.

These examples of Laura and Shirley show how important are the feelings of the parents in molding the character of the child. But these examples should not be considered as further evidence for the popular misconception that "all pretty girls get into trouble." This statement implies that it is the girl's beauty that gets her into trouble. However, this misconception really tells the girl who knows that she is pretty that she might be permitted to do things that the other girls must not do. Standards of conduct should be the same for all girls and women, regardless of their beauty. The comeliness of the girl, which in itself is a desirable characteristic, easily lends itself to distortion in this way by society, the parents and the girl herself. With her beauty and her physical attraction to men, the means for carrying out such behavior are more readily available to her. Through the girl's beauty, her parents might more easily find a readily excusable and available outlet for their own distorted needs than with a less beautiful girl. But, if such excuses or means were not available, others would be found, because such behavior originates from the parents' attitudes which do not depend upon the physical appearance of the child.

Joe's sister, Betty, had been gradually prepared for the change to womanhood by a healthy, honest relationship with her mother. In contrast, Joe was supposed to learn things for himself. After all, he was a boy. This was not a subject he would or should have discussed with his mother. His father was either too busy or unapproachable. Yet, Joe was growing up. He had the same problems in general that Betty had. Joe was getting taller and heavier; his external genitals were enlarging; hair was appearing on his body; his shoulders were getting broader; and his voice was getting deeper. These were the visible changes, but Joe was also beginning to show an increasing interest in girls, and he began to take greater pride in his own physical appearance. As a matter of fact, Joe seldom spent less time combing his hair in front of the mirror than did his sister. He showed the same attention to the clothes he wore and the way he wore them. It was also at this time that another aspect of Joe's development became more apparent. He both wished to be like everyone else in his group, and at the same time, he wished to compete with and be better than the others. "All the fellows in school are wearing red jackets."

In contrast with Johnny's sister, nothing had ever been said to Johnny before this. "Did not the textbooks say that girls really develop earlier than boys? For that matter, boys can shift for themselves better than girls and can learn from one another . . . and anyway, Johnny has never asked. He must not think much of these things. He's too young." Finally, Mr. and Mrs. Brown decided that their son, Johnny, was sufficiently grown up so that Mr. Brown should systematically review the subject of sex with his son.

"Come into the living room with me, Johnny; I want to tell you some things you should know!" Mother was conspicuously absent as she remained in the kitchen with younger brother, Tom, as though by a prearranged signal. Johnny sensed that his father was flustered and did not know quite how to begin. Mr. Brown finally cleared his throat and with a sheepish look, blurted, "John, your mother tells me you've been thinking of girls lately. Is there anything about them you'd want to know?" It seemed that Mr. Brown approached this problem with his son with the same bluntness and clockwork precision that he used in his work as an accountant. He was embarrassed; so was his son. Johnny had many questions; he had had them for years; but he never would ask them of his parents. The son clearly sensed, as he had all along, that his father would prefer to leave the topic alone. However, acting as though it were a chore to be completed as quickly as possible, Mr. Brown fumbled his way through a discourse on sex. Johnny kept his eyes on the floor; he was too upset to understand what was said. He asked no questions. At the end of the monologue, Mr. Brown picked up a book and handed it to his son, "Here, read this! It told me all I needed to know. If you have any questions after you've read it, you can always come to me."

It is just as important for a boy as it is for a girl to have the parent of the same sex instruct him on the subject. Both boys and girls have these questions as they grow up. If they feel comfortable with their parents and if they sense that their parents will answer these questions honestly and without embarrassment or punishment, the children will ask these questions when they occur to them. Such honesty and lack of embarrassment by the parents encourage future questions. Sex will be viewed in its proper perspective as another phase of the process of growing up. It will not be shunned as a topic of shame nor will it receive the undue interest usually accorded to that which is expressly forbidden. Obviously, Johnny could not profit from the formal and rigid lecture given by his father. Johnny sensed his parents' feelings that sex is a shameful and unclean subject that should not be discussed. Having been subjected to these values throughout his formative years, from the first romance stage on, Johnny had long since accepted these values as his own. But his curiosity demanded some measure of satisfaction. Unable to turn to his parents for the information which he most earnestly sought, he had to depend upon his friends for whatever information he could obtain. Such information is all too often distorted by half-knowledge, superstition and lurid sensationalism. If the parent feels uncomfortable about answering a child's question about sex (and this is common), the parent should turn to the physician for help in this matter.

The nocturnal emission (wet dream) represents the male sexual discharge which leaves a slightly discolored starchy area with a definite odor on the bed sheet. Like the appearance of menstruation in a girl, the wet dream is a healthy sign of approaching physical maturity in the boy. So far as nature is concerned, the boy is then approaching manhood and soon will be capable of becoming a father.

Mothers often volunteer their mistaken belief that their sons must be having this discharge as a result of handling the external genitals. The mother also often recalls that as a young child the boy used to place his hands in the region of his external genitals whenever he was tense. The mother may have scolded her son for doing so and warned him that he would hurt himself or suffer other harm if he persisted in such activity. However, boys and girls often handle their genitals during their childhood. When a boy does so before 3 years of age, it has the same meaning to him as handling his ears, nose or any other part of his body. It is at this time that he is curious about his own body and is busy exploring it. From 3 to 6 years of age, such handling may be accompanied by vague pleasurable physical sensations (masturbation) which he does not understand, which do not have the same relationship, in thoughts and feelings, to the opposite sex that similar behavior has in puberty and later life. If such extremely unhealthy erotic associations occur at this early age, they could only have been learned from the parents. The same is true of girls during these age periods. Beyond 6 years of age, such activity can occur occasionally and should cause no undue alarm. However, when it is noted almost incessantly, it is suggestive of the child's having some tension with which he cannot cope directly. He must then revert to an earlier mode of behavior for pleasure and relief of such tension (see p. 68). If he is getting what he should out of life in his relations with other people (especially with his mother and father), tension does not build up, and he need not look for relief by masturbation or other outlets (for example, thumb-sucking, nail-biting and temper tantrums). The same general rule holds for adolescents. However, at puberty, the boy can also relieve his tension through masturbation, but in a more complex way. At this time, the tension is often in the sexual sphere, and the boy can have frank fantasies of different women and situations that stimulate him during masturbation. Such behavior at this time of life is more consciously related to the boy's sexual interests. Such behavior may normally persist off and on until marriage. Again, the same is true of girls during this age period.

While adolescence is a prelude to that which will follow, the attitudes of this stage of development are in turn wholly dependent upon the attitudes of the earlier stages, the mouth, the bowel, and the first romance stages.

CHAPTER 5

*P*unishment

Much is said and written about love—and rightfully so. It lends itself easily to discussion and tramples on the feelings of very few people. However, before one can love, one must first have received love. And one can give love more freely and fully if one has not been tragically wounded by many significant experiences that can lead only to hate. In such a sick individual, love can only follow a purging of this pre-existing hate. This cannot be done by merely saying to oneself, "I will not hate; I will love." The individual must first learn to recognize hate. Why does he himself hate? What are the manifestations of this hate? Only then, when the individual understands the meaning of hate, can he rid himself of it and be ready to receive and give love. People just do not get sick from "too much love."

Stubbornness is a way of showing one's anger. By refusing to do what another person wishes, one effectively combats the other individual and does so without violence. For example, children with a perfectionistic mother who makes strict demands which must be obeyed immediately and to the letter are angry whether they show anger or not. However, this anger may not come out directly but more deviously as stubbornness. This stubbornness may become established as a pattern of behavior and become directed toward people and situations that have nothing to do with the mother. In this manner, the original anger toward the mother becomes directed toward others. The child may not even be aware that he is angry nor does he remember the people or the situations against which the anger was directed originally. He is merely stubborn. Such spilling over of anger onto other individuals and situations is not unusual. Every individual remembers times when he has been so angry with something or somebody that he has "taken it out" on others.

It is only after his uncontrollable outbursts of anger, when he has calmed down and might stop to think about it, that he realizes that he has permitted his anger against one individual or situation to spill out upon another individual. He may even feel ashamed that he did so or, rarely, may begrudgingly apologize to the innocent victim of his anger. He may excuse himself by saying that he was just too angry and did not know what he was doing. And the wronged individual probably would forgive him, remembering all too well that he himself has acted similarly in the past. This is a very common example taken from everyday life in which an individual's behavior is determined by a passion which he has bottled up within himself and now it seeks an outlet. At the same time, this individual, during the act, is often only dimly aware of the existence of this underlying passion or the real reason that he is behaving as he does. These people who show their longstanding, deep-rooted anger by stubbornness, frequently appear weak, ingratiating, and submissive as if in an effort to conceal their anger, not only from others but also from themselves.

Instead of showing anger by a stubborn refusal to comply, a child may also show anger by active hostility. This may take the form of the child's striking at the mother, the teacher, or other individuals who may or may not be the original cause of the anger. It may take the form of the child's becoming critical, sarcastic and foul-mouthed. The child may also develop a permanent "chip on his shoulder" and be suspicious of everyone. In certain specific situations to be discussed later, fire-setting and stealing may also be seen.

In most angry children, it should be emphasized that the child is harboring a long-smoldering rage in response to a specific home situation of one of the many unhealthy types previously described. This rage affects his attitudes toward situations and people outside the home and is an ever-present part of him. Such a child never forgets his anger or desire for revenge. Rarely is the child or the parent aware of the longstanding emotional disturbances between them that caused this anger. This constantly angry child might be the mean little girl in nursery school who pushes her playmates off the chair, takes their toys and leaves them crying. He might be the school bully constantly baiting smaller boys and tormenting girls not in play but in malice. He might be the adult who enjoys throwing his weight around and delights in punishing his family, friends and everyone with whom he comes into contact. He might be the tyrant of the home, the office or the factory. She might be the matriarch in the home, the highly competitive career woman or the prima donna. Their anger is constantly boiling over, and their only relief is in finding a subject for their anger, someone whom they can punish. These people derive no real pleasure in inflicting their cruelties; they derive only a temporary and partial relief of the inner turmoil caused by their anger. They are possessed of a devil.

On the other hand, the child or the adult who repeatedly suffers at the hands of the bully or the tyrant is commonly the object of much pity. Yet careful evaluation of the specific situation reveals that this individual often finds himself in the position to receive punishment. He may change his school, playmates, job or wife (or husband), but seemingly, as if by accident, the punishment and the suffering continue. This, however, is not chance. To the casual observer and to the long-suffering person himself, the hard-luck story is accepted at face value. However pitiful and tragic the actual situation may seem to be, there is no mystery, and there is no accident.

The individual who must constantly mete out punishment and the individual who must constantly receive punishment are both driven by a devil. The receiving of punishment satisfies a definite need, although the sufferer is usually unaware of this fact. There is the child (or the adult) who is always falling and being cut, bruised and banged up. There are children who always have accidents, and when they grow up the same story continues. They are called "accident prone" individuals. Everybody feels pity (and sometimes a little exasperation) as he listens to 12-year-old Sally describe in great detail and with apparent relish her numerous aches and pains and her countless trips to the doctor. This happens each time one sees her; one expects it. As her mother says, "Sally has never been afraid of doctors. Even when she was only 6 years old, she'd march into the office like a little soldier to receive her injections. Though I know she suffered terribly, she always smiled . . . never a peep out of her. I know she was very miserable and suffered a great deal of pain when her tonsils were taken out 6 years ago. She was a perfect lady and never cried. Sally has always acted years older than her age, and she can take punishment!"

Sally's mother has also suffered much and always has had countless ailments. Although she never complains, even a child can look at her face and know how much she is suffering. "Don't worry about me. You people go out and enjoy yourselves. I'll be all right. If it gets worse, I can call the doctor." Sally's mother has her top dresser drawer overflowing with more than 30 patent medicines. Every new newspaper advertisement sends her scurrying to the druggist with new hope. She always knows exactly what is wrong with her: "acid stomach; chronic constipation with run-down nerves; acute nervous exhaustion; several dislocated vertebrae with pressure on the pain nerves causing headache; abdominal cramps; lumbago; high blood pressure headache; fatigue from low blood pressure; blood anemia and vitamin deficiency; and monthly cramps from hormone deficiency." When the physician finds nothing physically wrong with her after careful examination, including full laboratory studies, she remains unconvinced. "I know there must be something wrong. Can't you operate? I don't mind if you think it will help me. I can stand the pain." The physician says in a friendly manner, "Emma, I understand how badly you feel, but your problem is terrible nervous tension, emotion. Surgery will not help."

Johnny continues to play with the neighborhood bully in spite of the repeated bloody noses and black eyes. Mr. D. remains on the job in spite of a tyrannical employer and refuses offers of better jobs elsewhere. Mrs. J. "has sacrificed herself all her life for her family" and, strangely enough, her children show no gratitude. If a child truly receives love without any strings attached, one would expect the child to show gratitude and love in return. As another example, Mrs. F., following the death of her alcoholic and brutal huband, marries Tom who drinks and beats her every Saturday night. All these people are receiving punishment either from other people or from themselves.

Both the people who give and those who receive punishment in the many examples above are suffering from the same basic mental disorder. One cannot exist without the other. If one has the need to punish, there must also be the one who has the need to be punished. In fact, both these needs often co-exist in the same individual. However, in some persons one need may be stronger and therefore more obvious than the other. Those who must punish are known as sadists, and those who must be punished are known as masochists.

Why this need to punish and be punished? These people frequently have no inkling that such a need exists. It is their way of life. They forgot how they got that way and would be surprised and offended if asked, "Why is it that you're always causing trouble?" or "Why is it that you always find yourself in trouble?"

These complex and highly individual problems are for the most part derived from the bowel period. As you will remember, it is at this time that one of the early major contests between parent and child can take place, and it is during this stage that many other learning problems are encountered as the child is taught to conform to the rules of society. The way the parent, who is more powerful than the child, manages the contest over bowel training is often an indication of the way the parent has managed previous learning problems and the way the parent probably will manage innumerable future learning problems. The parent's attitudes in such situations determine the child's later attitudes toward people: he gets along well, fights them or gives in. The later struggles can reinforce the child's responses to the earlier struggle; or, these later struggles, if handled in a healthy manner, can modify the results of any earlier unhealthy ones through socially acceptable channels.

In oversimplified terms, it can be seen how a child or an adult can have the need to punish as a result of deep-lying anger caused by unhealthy feelings from early parent-child experiences. It is more difficult to understand why the child or the adult needs punishment. One reason is shown by the parent who behaves in such a manner as to invite punishment as did Sally's mother, Emma. Such a parent, by her own example, may instill into the child similar values for determining behavior. However, this exceedingly complex need for punishment has many other poorly understood causes. A second reason is shown by the child or the adult who is angry and consequently might feel guilty; he then may need some form of punishment to assuage his deep-lying guilt. A third possible reason for needing punishment is provided by the example of the child who is being kept unnaturally dependent upon his parents. Although he may not even be aware of it, such a child is understandably angry at being kept in such continuous servitude. As a result of his long-standing abject dependency, he is completely helpless, afraid and unable to act independently; he always must seek out someone who will demand his complete submission and tell him what to do and when to do it. He must accept this abject dependency (punishment) to acquire the false security that he buys dearly at the sacrifice of his freedom and the containment of his resultant rage. His parents have completely blocked his development to a happy and full emotional maturity. By doing so, they have shown not the love that they profess but hate. And the child with his unhealthy extreme dependency has not the love which this dependency superficially appears to be but rather deep-lying hate. Neither parent nor child is ever quite aware of this fundamental hate. Such a child always must depend on someone.

A nondestructive expression of legitimate anger is a healthy response to a specific situation of which the child is fully aware. He is sticking up for his rights in a realistic fashion, and it is correct and healthy that he do so. It is important that his larger and stronger parents be fair and permit the child to express his anger in this manner when anger is justified. If they are wrong and the child is justifiably angry, the parents should not deny their wrong-doing but should be honest and admit to the child that they were wrong, that they are sorry and that his anger is perfectly understandable. This point of honesty between parents and child cannot be emphasized too strongly. No matter how small, helpless and inarticulate the child may be, he is a human being with all a human being's rights, feelings and emotions. These should be respected by those adults near to him who are entrusted with protecting and guiding the child to a healthy maturity. Permitting the child to express anger does not mean that the child ever should be permitted to strike his parents or commit any openly destructive acts as an expression of his anger. Such means of expressing anger never should be permitted under any circumstances.

There is equal reason for concern over the child who never shows anger or is not permitted by his parents to show anger. From previous and future examples in this book, one can see the results of the bottling up of justified anger.

Many parents, because of their own unhappy experiences with their own parents are unable to accept responsibility for their own actions, and when unpleasant situations develop for which they really are responsible, they may blame other people or situations unjustifiably. They are forever falling into the trap created by their own past experiences by excusing themselves and blaming others. With parents who are too ready to shift the blame elsewhere, the innocent and defenseless child is as vulnerable as his unfortunate parents were before him. Neither has ever known any other type of behavior from those close to him. In each instance, the child is offered no choice; he must accept the blame; he must not protest. Often, in such warped home situations it is too easy for such a parent to vent his pent-up emotions on the child who is defenseless rather than on someone else who may really be responsible for the parent's difficulty but who can fight back. The child will resent being blamed unfairly and being forced to accept his parent's wrath for things that he did not do. The child, unable to show his anger against his parents, must accept their blame, and the resultant anger can only be turned against himself. He becomes depressed. Or, he may copy his parent's solution by blaming others as the parent blamed him. In addition to the anger and the depression which often follow, such unhealthy parental attitudes also breed distrust and suspicion. Unable to trust his parents whose feelings and actions determine his own feelings and behavior, how can the child ever learn to trust anyone else? These changes occur so subtly and gradually that the victim hardly senses that they are present or that they are acting upon him. The effects are cumulative and, if progressive, very corrosive.

If this tendency to distrust and hate others becomes extreme, how can the child ever become friendly with other people; he distrusts and hates them, and they in turn are aware of and react to his underlying hostility with reciprocal mistrust and anger. The child has the perfect answer. He will think, "No one trusts me! They don't like me! I will neither trust nor like them!" Cause and effect have been reversed. Thus the child may blame others for situations which his own underlying attitudes have initiated and fostered. With time and progression of this emotional distortion, the child might become the patient who believes people persecute and accuse him of various misdeeds. With still further distortion, the patient might have hallucinations during which he hears voices accusing him of various misdeeds. He "knows" that someone is unduly influencing him with electrical machines and that his mind is being read. He is paranoid. There is, of course, quite a span between the angry child and the patient described above. There must be progression of the symptoms and repeated contact over the years with disturbing influences for this extremely disturbed paranoid state to develop. However, in paranoid patients studied under ideal conditions, the trail always leads back to an unhealthy parent-child relationship of the type described. It must be emphasized that lies shared between parents and children do not invariably lead to a paranoid state.

Although discipline of the child, when justified, is necessary, it never should be a subversion of the parents' own difficulties. For instance, the parent might mete out punishment out of all proportion to the misdeed of the child or without any infraction at all by the child. In this instance, it is the parent who must take his own tension out on someone. The child who cannot fight back is the victim. The rage of the alcoholic father who comes home drunk and whips both mother and child is a common example.

Less obvious but as far-reaching in its effects is the case of the unfortunate high-strung tense mother who gets along poorly with her husband and must work to help support her family. She needs an escape valve for her tension. Her young son is continually being yelled at, sent to his room, put to bed early and deprived of desserts and movies for numerous minor and fancied misdeeds.

From what has been said, there certainly is a time, a place and a way for the child to show justified anger and for the parent to scold or even whack the child when justified. It is not the physical injury of the slap or the child's anguish at being scolded but the feelings exchanged between parent and child that are all-important.

Physical punishment is seldom necessary in a child who has a healthy relationship with his parents. In such a relationship the child knows what he should and should not do. He knows that when his parents tell him something, they mean exactly that and not something else. The child respects his parents and is sure of their love; they in turn respect his needs and feelings as a human being. Their discipline is a simple direct appropriate response to a specific childish misdeed of which the child is fully aware. Such an honest parent will seldom have need to punish the child, and, when punishment is necessary, the parent will feel quite comfortable about it. Punishment is given for the child's sake and not for the sake of the parents.

CHAPTER 6

The Child Who Eats Too Much

Rudy P., 5 feet and 3 inches tall, weight 165 pounds and aged 12, came to the physician's office to receive his polio shot. He held his mother's hand and would not let go. He preferred his mother's hand to playing or talking with other children in the crowded waiting room. Yet he smiled all the time as he nibbled on a chocolate bar. When his mother got up to answer the nurse's routine questions, Rudy put down his mother's magazine and went with her. When a child cried inside the office, Rudy's mother turned and said, "The doctor's not going to hurt you, Rudy; he's just going to look at you; wait until you see the lollypop he has for you. If you're a good boy, Mommy will get you a banana split with a nice big walnut on top!" Rudy squinted at his mother, "No, Mommy, I don't want a banana split, I want a hot-fudge sundae . . . a hot-fudge sundae, Mommy."

Little 5-year-old Tim was playing on the waiting room floor. He looked up at Rudy and then turned to his mother, "Gee, Mommy, he's a fatso." Rudy bent his head forward, looked straight ahead, blushed, and munched on his chocolate bar faster. Mrs. P. squeezed Rudy's hand, twisted on the couch and effectively interposed her body between Tim and Rudy. Rather self-consciously she asked the nurse: "How many times will Rudy have to come for his polio shots?"

"Mommy, I got to go—I got to go." . . . "Just a few minutes, Rudy, and we'll be inside." . . . "No, Mommy, I can't wait, I can't wait." Nurse Dotty directed Mrs. P. and Rudy to the lavatory. Mrs. P. went in with him. When they returned to the couch, the chocolate was gone, but Rudy was busy chewing his nails.

Nearby, two waiting mothers were discussing their children's repeated colds and earaches that past winter. Mrs. P. entered the conversation by proudly exclaiming that her son was in such good health that this was his first visit to the doctor since his preschool examination 7 years previously. "I've never had any trouble with Rudy. He's a model child, perfectly obedient and eats everything I put in front of him." The other two waiting mothers looked at Rudy and smiled.

Two-year-old Dianne came toddling over, stared at Rudy and offered him her lollypop. Rudy remained impassive. Dianne's mother pulled her away angrily, saying, "That's yours, Honey; you keep it! I'm sure his mother doesn't want him to take any more." Her anger reverted to a tolerant smile. Rudy's mother could not miss the hint of criticism and said; "I know he's a little chubby now, but all boys are fat at this age. He'll outgrow it when his glands mature!"

Nurse Dotty finally beckoned Rudy and his mother into the office after a wait that seemed endless. The physician looked up, "Now what have we here? You sure are a big boy, aren't you, fellow?" Mrs. P. broke in, "I've never had any trouble with his appetite, Doctor, but, of course, as you know, it's just his glands." Rudy cried out, "Don't let the Doctor give me a shot, Mommy . . . please, Mommy, no shot!" Mrs. P. shushed Rudy and continued, this time without any interruptions from an obedient Rudy. "Please excuse my little boy, Doctor. He's not half as good as Marge, his sister, that way. Nothing frightens her. Why, she'd come into your office, know all your patients, play with the toys and then take the shot without a whimper. But she's different from Rudy. She's like me that way. She's built like me too . . . slender . . . always on the go. That girl doesn't stop from morning to night. Someday she'll make some lucky man a wonderful wife and mother. The women in my family have always had good figures. People always thought Mother and I were sisters. I guess they'll make the same mistake between Marge and me."

Unable to get in a word until now, the physician asked about Rudy's father. Mrs. P. blurted, "All men are alike though . . . my own father was the same way." The physician looked confused and hesitantly repeated his question. "That's what I mean, Doctor; Rudy's Daddy lives for only two things —food and sleep. No ambition at all. Funny thing, after seeing Mother suffer with my father, I always promised myself it would not happen to me. I guess sometimes we marry too young.

"Take the doctor's pencil out of your mouth, Rudy. He's always got something in his mouth, Doctor, I can't stop him. He's always got to eat between meals. When I want him to talk to strangers, he always clams up. At home he'll never stop chattering. If I take food away from him, he sulks and says, 'You don't love me, Mommy!'"

Realizing that Rudy's troubles were probably deep-rooted, the physician did not know quite where to begin. He wondered, from her statements so far, whether Rudy's mother might not have considerable emotional confusion toward men which in turn might be reflected in Rudy's obesity. Therefore, the physician gave Rudy his shot, and strongly urged Mrs. P. to make an appointment for Rudy on a day when there was sufficient time for a complete investigation. The physician emphasized that the problems of obesity were often due to emotional rather than physical causes, but without a complete history and examination of Rudy and without doing any of the indicated laboratory procedures, he would be unable to be more specific at that time. He also said that sometimes the correction of these conditions, physical or emotional, which cause obesity is as important as immunizing a child against a disease. Mrs. P. smiled most ingratiatingly and agreed to do as the physician suggested. Then she left, promising to phone Nurse Dotty later for an appointment. Rudy was not seen again, not even for his second polio shot.

This case history brings up many points which should be further discussed individually. Despite Rudy's obvious overweight, his mother brought him to the physician for polio shots and not for the obesity. Her seeming refractoriness to the problem of Rudy's obesity was really quite elusive. Her response to the thinly veiled sarcasm of the other mothers and the not-so-innocent taunts of 5-year-old Tim gave some indication that she was far more aware of the existence of this problem than her proud denial would admit. Her physician, perceiving that this was a complex problem with many explosive emotional undertones, treaded gently with kindness and understanding in these disturbed waters. Nevertheless, his honest and matter-of-fact approach which was purposely gentle and superficial at this initial visit was unable to overcome her fears of what a sincere discussion of the roots of the problem might divulge. She could only smile in apparent agreement to her physician's suggestion, but her real reactions were revealed when she failed to return.

Mrs. P.'s extreme touchiness about Rudy's obesity was also revealed by her prolonged rambling response to the physician's greeting to her son. She immediately silenced Rudy's protests, disregarded his fears and proceeded to talk about herself. This reaction graphically but strongly hinted at her complete indifference to her son and his problems and her preoccupation with herself. The physician began discussing her son; the mother talked about herself. So far as could be seen, her chief avenue of communication with Rudy was on a very immature level. Although 12 years old, Rudy always held his mother's hand, talked like a baby and responded to upsetting situations by the "mouth stage" mode of behavior: eating chocolate bars, sucking lollypops, bargaining with his mother for a chocolate fudge sundae, chewing his fingernails and gnawing on the doctor's pencil. His mother encouraged all of this.

Mrs. P. said that she loved her son. However, this apparently meant that she fed him, because if Rudy were really comfortable and secure in the love of his mother, there would be no need for him to resort to the use of an earlier mode of behavior continuously. From her rambling monologue and without attempting to get a complete picture, the physician again received the definite impression that Mrs. P. was a very strong-willed woman who imagined herself to be perennially young and attractive. In boastfully comparing her daughter with Rudy, Mrs. P. was really extolling her own virtues. In her brief and scattered allusions to the men and the women in her family, the description of the women was highly complimentary while that of the men was derogatory. Her marital dissatisfaction was also strongly hinted at by her description of her husband as a rather placid, easy-going man of no ambition for whom she felt not love or respect but only contempt. Ironically enough, her mother felt the same way about her own husband, Mrs. P.'s father. Beneath the facade of solicitousness for Rudy, there were the facts: Rudy was fat, would not mix with children his own age and was completely dependent upon his mother—an extremely unhealthy situation. Her hardly flattering appraisals of her husband, father and son, indicated her own poor adjustments with men. Her complimentary appraisals of her mother, daughter and herself strongly indicated her superficial view of femininity: the facade of a good figure represents femininity. Finding himself in a family whose women were unfriendly to men and whose men could not assert themselves with women, Rudy never would know any alternative to the docile submission of men to women.

Rudy responded as might be expected. He adopted the attitudes that his mother had toward men. His own estimate of himself was contemptuous. He completely complied with his mother's wishes and needs which required that men be kept subservient. She could not help feeling as she did; these feelings depended upon her own early upbringing. Rudy ate the food that his mother substituted for genuine affection and respect for men. This became his way of life; he became fat and remained helplessly dependent like a baby. When confronted with any of life's many problems, Rudy showed no outward signs of emotion nor could he attempt to solve the problem by any appropriate reaction toward the specific situation. However, faced with a problem, Rudy did develop tension which needed relief. He found an outlet for this tension through his own body in the way he had first learned with his mother while a little baby in the mouth stage. He ate, and he continued to eat until the situation that caused the tension changed and his tension disappeared. The situation could be—as it was in Rudy's case—the unhealthy parent-child feelings in the home which had their tragic effect on Rudy. Since these feelings never changed, Rudy continued to eat. Placid like his father and submissive to his mother, Rudy was physically inactive. He used less energy (calories) in the physical exertions of his daily life than the amount that he ingested daily in his food. He became swathed in fat.

His mother's personal problems and self-doubts were partially resolved at the expense of Rudy's needs and growing-up; he became an obese, shy, socially backward, dependent boy with a complacent smile but no happiness. Forever doomed to eat as a means of assuaging tension and forever the brunt of jokes, Rudy was laughed at but never with.

It may seem strange to the reader that there has been no mention so far of the popularly ascribed causes of obesity, causes that are more palatable to parents (and adult obese patients) than emotional ones. In an overwhelmingly large proportion of cases of obesity, the cause is eating too much, and eating too much for the exercise one does. "But Doctor, everything Tommy eats turns to fat. He eats no more than Johnny, the same age, but Johnny isn't fat." In most cases, this statement is a gross exaggeration of the facts.

It is well known that fat people do not generally engage in the more competitive physical activities. "Chubby" plays marbles well, but he is not wanted on the neighborhood baseball team; he is too slow. This physical inactivity, however, is quite secondary in importance to the overeating. Eating depends on hunger and appetite. Hunger is determined by the body's actual need for growth and living. Appetite, on the other hand, indicates the pleasure of eating (as contrasted with the physical need for food). Appetite is highly variable and is determined almost solely by how one feels. When one is temporarily sick with fever, angry or depressed, appetite may decrease. When such feelings get out of control and persist, decreased appetite and subsequent weight loss appear. Physicians frequently see depressed patients who are slowly "wasting away." When one feels gay, satisfied with the world or well rested, he indulges his appetite. However, there are emotionally disturbed patients who eat not less but more, as in Rudy's case. These individuals use eating as a means of assuaging tension just the way that children frequently revert to thumb-sucking when faced with an emotionally disturbing situation. Thus, if such people stop overeating, for any of various reasons, without changing their basic emotional structure, they may develop a serious depression with, in some instances, an accompanying risk of suicide.

It was noted that the physician, although suspecting the emotional basis of Rudy's obesity, insisted on a complete examination, including necessary laboratory tests, to establish the cause. He knew that very rarely brain tumors and infections, glandular disturbances and certain diseases can cause body changes that might be mistaken for obesity. But, such cases are rare. He also recognized that what our culture so often classifies as obesity is really a hereditary stockiness in body build. In such people the physical proportions, which may not be currently fashionable, are completely appropriate and healthy for that particular individual. Rudy's physician, knowing his patient's family and noting the obvious extreme overweight, recognized that Rudy's problem was more than simple hereditary stockiness. In most patients, adult and child, obesity is due to overeating; overeating depends on appetite; appetite depends on emotion.

A rare dread condition which is more serious than obesity, because life itself is jeopardized, is "anorexia nervosa" (nervous loss of appetite). In this condition, the reverse of the fundamental feeding mechanisms noted in the obese child is seen. In such patients, there is nothing wrong with the brain, the glands or the stomach. The appetite is greatly decreased as a result of deeply rooted emotional conflicts which frequently go back to infancy and childhood. These patients completely lose all interest in their family, friends, acquaintances, home, work, dress and so on. They lie on the bed, a depressed bag of bones, totally disinterested in the world about them. In children, most cases appear at or shortly after puberty when the pre-existing parent-child conflicts become intensified.

CHAPTER 7

How Bowel Training
Influences Character Traits

Why do people worry so much about their bowels?
Why do people attach so much significance to bowel function?

"Doctor, my child does not have a bowel movement every
day." "Doctor, my child's bowel movements are too hard."
And with some such introduction by the mother, 9-year-old
Johnny may interject a detailed description of his bowel habits. Grandmother, who so often worries about her own bowel
habits and feels that there is a direct relationship between
her own health and her bowel regularity, is also frequently
worried about her grandchildren's bowel movements. The
frequent use of enemas, suppositories and laxatives to initiate
bowel movements is taken as an unquestioned part of life's
routine. Pick up any newspaper or magazine in any language,
and one will find an advertisement for a laxative.

An old wives' tale is that a child must have a bowel movement every day on schedule. This is a complete fallacy. A
child (or an adult) may have a bowel movement every other
day, twice a day or every 3 days and be completely normal
in this respect. Bowel habits vary from person to person
within a wide range of normal. The consistency and not the
frequency is the important thing. If the stool stays in the
bowel too long before being passed, the body absorbs more
and more water from the stool, and the stool becomes harder
and harder. Constipation results. Therefore, if a child (or
an adult) has only one bowel movement every 3 days and the
stool is of normal consistency, it should be no matter for con-

65

cern for that particular child (or adult). Another child (or
adult), however, may pass a "stoney" hard constipated stool
with difficulty and often with discomfort, every 2 or 3 days
(or even every day). That is not normal. A physician often
sees the child whose parent (or grandparent) insists that the
child is constipated when, in fact, no constipation or bowel
disturbance of any type exists. Many adults (and children)
mistake a normal, easily passed stool for constipation only because it is firm and formed. The consistency of the stool is
determined by the type of food one eats, the amount of fluid
one drinks and one's activities and bowel habits. When food
of high bulk content is taken, the stool will become bulkier;
therefore, it will act like a sponge, "hold on" to water and remain soft. Naturally, drinking much fluid increases the bulk
and the softness of the stool.

Mrs. K. knows that her little cocker spaniel will have a
bowel movement after eating. She would not dare leave him
in the house after a feeding until he has had a chance to run
about outside and do his business. However, Mrs. K. does not
know what to do about her 8-year-old Jimmy. He eats, runs
outside to play, has a normal desire to move his bowels—but
he is too busy playing to go back into the house to heed
nature's call. He holds back; the desire passes; the stool remains in his bowel; fluid is absorbed from the stool; the stool
becomes very hard and firm—constipation results. Mrs. K.
apparently does not realize that after eating, the child, like
the dog, has a normal desire to move his bowels; the particular meal, breakfast, lunch, or supper, after which this desire
occurs, varies from person to person. In dealing with her
child, the mother should take advantage of this natural phe-
nomenon.

Enemas, laxatives and suppositories are artificial aids to be
used on rare occasions and not as a matter of routine. If a
person's bowel habits have suddenly changed or if he must
continually depend on artificial aids, including various patent
medicines, a physician should be consulted. If the child has
true constipation that persists, then the physician will detail
the application of these general principles—if his examination

reveals that the constipation is due to bad habits and not to disease.

"Brenda has been irritable all day. Let's give her some 'magnesia.' That always works!" Newspaper advertisements and old wives' tales to the contrary, when a person feels fatigued, irritable and sluggish, she feels so because of disease or what is going on around her and not because of her bowels. The medical facts are exactly the opposite of the popular concepts. For example, if Brenda becomes irritable, her stools may in turn become constipated. On the other hand, Ralph's loose bowel movements may be a physical expression of his concern over the coming tests in school. Frequently, constipation or diarrhea may follow various states of emotional unrest. The newspaper and magazine advertisements that imply that sluggish bowels cause a sluggish mind and emphasize bowel regularity as a prerequisite to health, merely exploit popular misconceptions and half-truths. That such remedies relieve the complaint does not mean that the constipation causes the complaint. Returning to Brenda, her irritability may respond to the "magnesia," but her problem is as effectively— and deplorably—handled by her grandmother who slaps her on the face and tells her to get busy with her play and stop getting in the way. In many cases, laxatives, suppositories and especially enemas amount to nothing more than punishment. Brenda is frightened out of her complaints. If she does complain, she'll be slapped again—or given another enema.

Although many children are repulsed by laxatives, suppositories and enemas or the threat of them, many other children associate completely different feelings with such interference with their bowel function. Such children look forward to the laxatives, the suppositories and the enemas or, incredibly, may even request them, but they do not know why they do so. They will offer, in all earnestness, what they believe to be the reasons, but they are not the real reasons. These strange ideas do not arise from the child himself but are acquired from the grownups around him.

Returning to the discussion on the bowel stage of development, the reader will recall how, during this stage, the child normally derives great pleasure from bowel movements. As he matures, this pleasure is replaced by other forms of pleasure more in keeping with his advancing years.

As has already been shown in this book, if the parent-child relationships are unhealthy, the child may be more comfortable by remaining fixed, feeling-wise, in this earlier stage of development than by proceeding to the more dangerous and threatening later stages. In this manner, the child will avoid the feelings and the rivalries inherent in the coming first romance stage. He is unable to face these new feelings and rivalries, because the parent's own emotional difficulties have tainted the parent-child relationship. Despite the great effect of these feelings and rivalries upon the individual, he is only dimly aware of their presence or crucial action in determining his behavior.

On his own, the child always will attempt to go forward with his emotional (as with his physical) growth. As he matures, the child will meet new feelings and experiences. In some instances, these will come up against unhealthy attitudes or touchy areas in his parents' emotional make-up, and these will prevent the child from progressing in a fully healthy manner. As a result, the child is confronted with unhealthy solutions. By behavior and feelings, the parents can permit the child to advance in a totally unhealthy manner consistent with their own warped needs. Or, the child may be permitted to retreat to safer feelings and modes of behavior associated with earlier stages of emotional development when the parent-child relationship was less threatening. However, at the same time, the child's unfolding personality will also meet parental attitudes which are quite healthy. In these regions, the child will acquire the healthy aspects of his parents' personality. Therefore, as he advances to the next stage of development, the child will acquire, in some areas, the healthy aspects of his parents' personality while in other areas he will be forced to make an unhealthy adjustment with his parents' unhealthy feelings. Both parents and child are only dimly aware of why they really act as they do.

When the first romance stage appears with all its accompanying emotional values and pleasures, the child be-

comes more interested in other people of the same and opposite sex. He outgrows his earlier interest in himself and his
body (i.e., bowels). He need no longer depend chiefly on his
own body and its functions to gratify his needs. But if the
child's parents, for reasons of their own, attach unnaturally
important values to the functions and the pleasures of the
bowel stage, for example, the child will acquire, as already
shown, similar values.

If at any time in his later life, in his relations with people,
the child is confronted with a frightening or intolerable situation that defies solution, tension builds up. Without even
being aware of it, he will remember the great pleasures and
comforts originally derived from his own body at the bowel
stage of development. He will show an increased interest in
the needs and the pleasures of this stage (his own body) for
relief of his tensions. But the relief is not complete. The fears
and the disappointments which he had experienced at the
more advanced stage of emotional development will continue
to haunt him even after his return to the bowel stage. Instead
of difficulties with people, he will have difficulties with his own
bowels: constipation, diarrhea and numerous complaints of
aches and pains in this region of the body.

Development is a continuous process with overtones of the
past continually seeping into the present. These processes
of fixation at or regression to earlier stages of development are
seldom complete. They are a patchwork of variable changes.
The feelings of both the earlier and the later stages of development are inextricably mixed together and determine the
child's feelings and modes of behavior as well as his ways of
obtaining pleasure. Therefore, the child may show many
feelings derived from the first romance stage of development
while also maintaining a keen interest and deriving much
pleasure from his bowel function. This child may grow up,
meet and marry someone and then become a parent. His
children may in turn acquire the same interest and pleasure in
bowel function. The wheel has completed another turn; the
attitudes of one generation have been passed on to the next.

As any mother remembers, the young infant is not disgusted by soiling himself. In fact, if the mother is not quick enough, the child, through his own natural curiosity, will touch and handle his stools. The mother becomes excited at the mess that the child makes; the child shows only his natural interest in his body and its products. Watch the 1-year-old having a bowel movement, and, provided that there is no associated pain, he may grunt and smile. There is relief of the urge to move his bowels and actual pleasure in the act. But soiling oneself and soiling oneself whenever and wherever one wishes to do so is not socially acceptable. The growing child must learn to conform to the dictates of the culture in which he lives. In the child's narrow world, the parents represent this culture. Their demands and wishes should mirror the demands and the wishes of society. By obeying his parents, he will learn to act so that he can become an acceptable member of society. This process of learning, then, consists of two factors: the child must curb his natural desire for pleasure when it conflicts with his parents' habits, and he must remember what his parents said he should and should not do. He is developing a conscience, which is based, however, on his parents' own consciences. If the child's conscience is to develop properly, his parents' consciences must be sound. If the parents' consciences are tainted so will be that of their child.

If his mother is gentle and understanding in her training, he will surrender the childish pleasure of moving his bowels where and when he wishes in return for her love, and he will surrender comfortably and go forward without ill effects in his development. If there is any emotional undercurrent between mother and child, it is at this stage of acquiring independence that the child finds a strong weapon with which to strike back at his mother. He can soil in the wrong places and at the wrong times; he can refuse to move his bowels at all (and constipation results). By these methods, the child can exert real power over his mother. In the final analysis, despite all the mother's wishes, pleadings and commands, they are the child's own bowel movements to be passed when and where he chooses to do so. Here is an excellent way for the little child to show his anger and punish his mother by not doing what she wishes.

Recognizing the values attached to bowel movements by the parents and the child, it can be seen why the child, previously bowel-trained, may begin to soil. Four-year-old Libby began to soil shortly after her newborn baby sister was brought home. With all the subsequent attention paid to the baby by the parents and the visitors, Libby, previously the only child, and the recipient of all attention, feared the loss of parental love. Gradually, as Libby became aware that her parents sincerely loved both her and the baby, soiling disappeared. There was no further need for Libby to depend upon the pleasures of the earlier bowel stage. This is a very common example of the way a child may return to the pleasures of an earlier stage for relief of intolerable tension.

Five-year-old Tommy's parents were both killed in an automobile accident, and Tommy had to be placed in an orphanage. Suddenly and tragically robbed of his parents and their love upon which he depended, Tommy began to soil. It was only after Tommy learned that he was not alone, that someone cared for and loved him, that the soiling gradually ceased.

There are, of course, other specific causes for soiling. From what has already been said in this chapter, some cases of soiling, as in the above examples of Libby and Tommy, are temporary and of minor importance; they will disappear with time. Other cases, however, are more persistent and depend upon deep-seated and serious emotional disturbances between parent and child and frequently require treatment for both. In extremely rare instances, factors other than emotional may be the cause of soiling; they can be recognized by the physician.

When the child learns bowel control, he might develop many personality scars stemming from conflicts over bowel-training which he lost to his mother. As a result of these early upsetting experiences, several possibilities may be seen. The child's early disturbing experience with his first person in authority, his mother, may influence his relations with all people in authority (teacher, preacher, physician, employer, policeman, judge and lawyer) whom he meets later in life. He will meet them with the same attitudes that he originally had toward his mother: either a stubborn, active defiance or a passive acquiescence and noncompliance.

The exchange of feeling between mother and child at the bowel stage as at other periods of development is all-important. No one would doubt that cleanliness is learned as is bowel-training. The mother's rigid and forced insistence that the child be bowel-trained, that the child "stay clean," and this as perfectly as possible and at as early an age as possible, reflects the mother's rigid, uncompromising and perfectionistic standards. There can be no deviation. The child can get along with his mother only by strict obedience to her rigid standards. This insistence on early and perfect cleanliness can become a fixed, ever-present idea—an obsession (in this case, an obsession for cleanliness). In addition to the child's obsession, he is bound by the memory of his mother's perfectionism and orderliness. This perfectionism spills over and taints related character traits which develop as the child grows older.

The doting relatives think it is wonderful that Mary is so fussy and insists that everything "must be just so," like her mother. Mary repeats and practices endlessly, but she has such unrealistic standards of perfection that she can seldom finish what she starts. Mary is scrupulously clean in her grooming, clothes and room. She is always on time and very proper in her speech. Everything follows a definite schedule which may not be changed. What appears so efficient is really a ritual. If her daily pattern becomes interrupted in any way, she "goes to pieces" and does not know what to do in the new situation. She cannot adapt herself to changing conditions. She is very unsure of herself and asks endless questions to make certain that she does things exactly right. These countless and repeated questions enrage her mother. Yet, Mary's questions are really the same sort of "right or wrong," "yes or no," "good or bad" questions that her mother continually asks her. "Did you close the window in your room? . . . are you sure? . . . did you brush your teeth? . . . are you sure? . . . there is still a smell on your breath . . . did you have a bowel movement yet this morning? . . . was it constipated? . . . did you wash your hands before dinner . . .?

It should be noted that Mary's mother worried about the odor of Mary's breath. Insofar as the mother's concern is within reason, the question is natural, but giving undue attention to the problem is unnatural. People who are obsessed with cleanliness also make a big point of odors. Odors are a manifestation of cleanliness or uncleanliness. Such people cannot stand bad odors and will go to all extremes to eliminate them. And they take exceptional delight in pleasant odors. Their reactions in this as in other behavior traits (cleanliness, punctuality, perfectionism, orderliness) are exaggerations of the concern seen in the healthy individual.

All these character traits which have apparently so little in common and occur in all individuals to a greater or lesser extent, appear during the bowel stage of development as a result of the example and the attitudes of the grownups. The parent's example and attitudes at this time will determine whether the child will grow up a healthy individual constructively using these traits or whether he will be victimized by them.

Complaints of the digestive tract (which includes the bowel) may be due to emotional problems, physical disease of the bowels or other organs and some of the many physical diseases which are influenced by the emotions. Two of the diseases of the digestive tract which are influenced by the emotions are peptic ulcer and chronic ulcerative colitis.

Peptic ulcer is a condition in which the stomach or the first portion of the small intestine (duodenum) has a punched-out, raw area of varying size in its lining. This disease which is so common in grownups is, fortunately, very rare in children. However, in recent years, more cases have been recognized in children. Like the grownup, the child with this disease also has many emotional problems which either contribute to the cause or aggravate the disease. Together with diet, drugs and surgery, the emotional needs of the patient must also be cared for in treating this disease.

Chronic ulcerative colitis is a serious disease of the large intestine which is found in adults much more frequently than in children. This condition is characterized by frequent, painful, loose bowel movements and many tiny bleeding areas in the large intestine. This disease of unknown cause is commonly associated, in the child, as in the adult, with serious emotional problems. In many cases it is felt that the early parent-child problems are very important factors that must be considered in the total management of such a patient by the physician.

CHAPTER 8

Stuttering, Left-handedness, Tics

The first definite sounds, "Mama," "Dada," "baba," that the child makes, commonly appear toward the end of the first year. The child, with these early sounds, begins learning speech in the first year of life, the mouth stage of emotional development. This speech-learning process continues throughout the rest of childhood—the bowel and the "first romance" stages of emotional development—and throughout life. It might be expected, then, that any emotional conflict arising during any of these stages may be reflected in the developing ability to speak; stuttering may develop. The child first learns to speak at the time he is giving up the bottle but when he still sucks, spits, bites and makes various new sounds with his lips, cheeks, vocal cords and tongue. In turn, the making of these new sounds depends upon learning breath control. He is a creature who stumbles, falls, crawls, wobbles and toddles, but, through it all, he slowly learns to walk. His first few "steps" in talking are similarly awkward and unsure. Yet he can watch his parents walk, and they can show him how to walk. The child can easily imitate walking; he can see it. He cannot "see" how to talk. He knows his father, mother and other family members, including the dog; he knows what is going on about him; and he perceives and reacts to the feelings that others have toward him. But he cannot put all this into words. His thinking develops faster than he can develop control over his muscles of speech. The control over these muscles is no further developed than his control over the muscles for walking, bowel movement or emptying the blad-

der. The awkwardness noted in walking and faulty control
over bladder and bowels is thus also present in his use of the
muscles of speech—tongue, lips, cheeks, diaphragm and vocal
cords. He stutters. All children stutter when they learn to
talk, even as they wobble when they learn to walk.

If stuttering continues beyond the learning stage, some
emotional difficulty may be at fault. This difficulty is to be
found in some conflict arising in the mouth, the bowel, or the
"first romance" stages of the child's development when the
major early part of speech learning occurs. It is obvious from
what has been said previously that in learning to talk it is the
feelings behind the words and not the actual words that are
important. In all of us, adult and child, certain words evoke
certain feelings based on what has happened to us or what has
been taught to us before. For example, the word "cow" might
evoke the feeling of quiet contentment; it is related to the
giving of milk. But if a child had been chased and frightened
by a cow, he might quake in fear whenever the word "cow"
is mentioned. If the situation and the consequent fear are
handled well by the parents, such a reaction should be only
temporary. The word "snake" to many people means a slimy,
twisting, crawling creature of fear; the word itself becomes a
symbol; it evokes unpleasant feelings. When a child is learning
a language, the important point is the emotional values and
purposes attached to the new words based on his own experiences or what his mother and father teach him. The mere
mechanics of speech, the vowels and the consonants and their
arrangement to form words are unimportant to the child. The
feelings are all-important.

Carol's brothers and sisters persistently tease her mercilessly
when she cannot make the "K" sound in her name. Carol
will have her self-confidence badly shaken, and speech will
become an emotional issue. She will dread speaking, and the
harder she tries, the more frightened she will become and the
more difficult it will be to speak. As time goes by, she will
forget, as will her parents, the original difficulty. Carol will
stutter whenever she tries to make the "K" sound. In addition
to the word "Carol," the difficulty in making the "K" sound
will spread to other words with the same sound: cat, catch,

cow, kite, come, kill. Some of these words, such as "kill," may have more emotion attached to them than other words such as "kite," and therefore the difficulty may be greater in some than in others. From what has been said, there are both specific and nonspecific causes for stuttering. Emotional tension stimulated directly by a specific word (teasing Carol as she learns to say her name) may cause stuttering with words having similar sounds.

Also, without his being completely aware of it, certain people may remind the child of unpleasant feelings that he may originally have had with some other specific person. The child may stutter when he talks to such people. In later life, John was usually quite fluent except when he had to speak to his boss, the policeman, or even a group of people who in the aggregate represented an authoritative body to him. John still carried his original fear, or possibly even anger, that he had harbored toward his perfectionistic, demanding and bullying father. In such a situation, while learning to talk and while under the domination of such a father, the young John understandably had feelings of rebellion and hatred. John dared not express any angry feelings toward his father lest he be bullied more. However, these pent-up feelings needed an outlet. The unintelligible biting, sputtering, spitting sounds of anger that he used as a baby became the stuttering of later life. When John was completely relaxed in friendly surroundings that evoked no unpleasant memories, there was no stuttering.

As a further but rarer example of the importance to the child of the feeling attached to words rather than the words themselves, compare the deaf mute in friendly and understanding surroundings with the patient with the mental disease, schizophrenia. The deaf mute who never has heard a word or spoken a word may grow up to become a happy, well-adjusted and useful member of society. For example, consider the remarkable accomplishments of Miss Helen Keller. In contrast, adult patients with schizophrenia occupy more hospital beds than patients with any other disease, mental or otherwise. This most common and complex disease of young adulthood is manifested in its extreme form by strange emotional reactions and thoughts which drift about in a "dream world" completely separate from the real world. So far as is known, there are no defects in intelligence or the senses. The earliest emotional roots of this disease lie in childhood, but this disease is rarely seen in children. Schizophrenia illustrates the importance that the words themselves have for the individual. For instance, some children with this very serious disease never utter a word until they are well beyond the age at which speech usually appears; at that time they may speak out in a perfectly articulated and grammatically correct short sentence. It is understood, of course, that there are many other causes for the late appearance of speech. One of the more common examples of this problem is that of the child who can effectively and quickly make his needs known without recourse to speech. Such a child has little incentive for learning to talk until later than the usual time. Other children with schizophrenia refuse to speak at all and may be mistaken for deaf-mutes. Still other children with this disease speak well mechanically and always have done so, but to the casual observer, they do not transmit feelings consistent with what they are saying. They may laugh while describing a situation that should evoke tears; they may cry when they should laugh. In the very common stuttering that all children have when first learning to speak, there is, as has been noted, already a temporary malalignment of the speech apparatus. This malalignment may persist if feelings become involved. The schizophrenic patient may or may not have difficulty with words, but he does have difficulty with his emotions. For him, it is neither the words themselves nor the mechanical articulation of speech that is important; it is the feelings which are attached to the words which are all important. But since the feelings of the schizophrenic patient are disturbed, he often associates different feelings and meanings with words or phrases than would a healthy individual. For this reason the schizophrenic patient reacts differently, feeling-wise, to certain words and phrases than does the healthy person, and that is why the healthy person often says that the schizophrenic patient reacts inappropriately. However, the reactions of the schizophrenic patient are entirely appropriate if one considers the particular emotions that he attaches to his words and phrases. It is as if he speaks his own peculiar language with sounds similar to those of the healthy individual but with different meanings.

In some cases of left-handedness, where the child has been forced to use his right hand, there appear various symptoms of emotional tension: nail-biting, thumb-sucking, tics, stubbornness, crankiness and stuttering. Although this problem of forcibly changing handedness, like stuttering in general, probably is due to the underlying emotional attitudes of the parents, there are other factors. As a simple example of the parental involvement, Jane wants to use her left hand to hold her spoon when eating. Her mother gently whacks the back of her left hand and firmly transfers the spoon to the right. Paul is very upset because his father, who is a civil engineer, insists that his son use his right hand in writing because, "I've never seen a left-handed engineer that was any damned good. You might as well learn correctly."

This is not to say that all children who are left-handed and are switched to the right hand will develop these difficulties. As a matter of fact, if the switch is accomplished early enough in life by parents who are friendly and understanding, it is likely that no emotional problem will result. If the child balks or becomes harassed at the change, the parents should not persist in their efforts but should leave the child alone.

In addition to the all-important underlying emotional attitudes in bringing about a change is the question of how deeply ingrained is the child's left-handedness. Does he go up the stairs with the left foot first, aim a pop-gun with his left eye, throw a ball left-handed or reach for the cookie jar with his left hand?

When Grandma had a stroke, the right side of her body was badly paralyzed. The worst thing of all was that she was not only unable to write, walk and care for herself, but she also lost the power of speech. She knew what was going on about her and what people were saying. She made many attempts to talk but did not succeed. Her physician told her family that Grandma's paralysis on the right side of the body was due to the blood clot in the left side of the brain and that he hoped that with time and treatment, Grandma would recover. Since the day of the famous Greek physician, Hippocrates, it has been known that damage to one side of the brain could account for the disturbed function of the opposite side of the body. Speech is impaired in a right-handed person only if the left side of the brain is damaged and, conversely, speech is impaired in a strongly left-handed person only if the right side of the brain is damaged. If the right side of the brain is damaged in a right-handed person, one would therefore expect that the left side of the body would be paralyzed, but the patient's speech is not affected. It is felt, then, that making a strongly left-handed child use his right hand will clash with the existing supremacy of the right side of the brain over the left side. In the child of school age, the brain pathways are already established, and an attempted change at this time may cause trouble more readily than if the change had been attempted at an earlier age. In addition to the parent's emotional attitudes, these are physical factors with which one must reckon.

The complex interplay of these forces, emotional and anatomic, may well result in stuttering and other previously mentioned nervous traits plus, in some cases at least, problems in reading, writing and arithmetic. As an extreme example, one may see the child who writes beautifully and correctly except for one flaw—nothing can be read unless a mirror is held to the writing; then one can read the words perfectly by looking into the mirror (mirror-writing). Another writing difficulty is the reversal of figures ("39" becomes "93"). Some of the reading difficulties are poor spelling and failure to understand the meaning of the printed word.

The relationship between right-handedness or left-handedness and these various difficulties in speech, reading and writing is evident, but the way in which this relationship works is obscure. More important to the child's developing personality is not whether he is left-handed or right-handed but the basic underlying feelings exchanged between the child and his parents.

In the age group of 6 to 10 years, it is commonly observed that children feel an urge to carry out certain acts in a repetitive manner. Thus one commonly sees a child who must step on a crack in the sidewalk or kick a rock ahead of him as he walks along, whack each post in a fence that he passes or count telephone poles. He may also insist that his shoes be lined up in a certain way, or he may feel the constant urge to clear his throat, blow his nose or scratch his ears. In the presence of emotional disturbances during these ages, it is not uncommon to see this tendency to repetitive acts become intensified and localized as a rigidly fixed habit.

Thus, "Helen is always jerking her left shoulder, Doctor; she has lost so much time from school. We don't know what is wrong. I know she can control it, because when we tell her to stop, she does so. Yet, the minute we turn our backs, it starts again. We wonder if it can be emotional. The jerking is worst when she meets strangers or when there is some argument in the home. When her father has some words with her, Helen says nothing . . . just turns away and goes to her room. But then that jerking starts again, worse than ever, and goes on for hours."

The physician spent much time carefully examining Helen. He noted that when Helen was relaxed and at ease with him, she appeared like any other 11-year-old girl with no unusual movements. This was quite striking, because only a few minutes before, when Mrs. D., Helen's mother, was describing the father's short temper with Helen, the movements were very pronounced. Helen would jerk her left shoulder upward and forward in short quick movements. The mother said these movements had begun when the father had playfully hit her on the left shoulder with a rubber beach ball 2 years before. Examination by the resort physician, including x-ray pictures taken immediately after the injury at the parents' insistence, had failed to reveal anything physically wrong. Since the movements continued, Helen's parents wanted to know if anything else could be done. The family physician checked Helen over very carefully; he made a complete examination, both physical and by special laboratory tests. There were no abnormalities other than the movements themselves. This was not surprising, since the physician, after carefully observing the movements that Helen's mother described and noting other slight movements that apparently had escaped the mother's notice, had felt reasonably sure that Helen had tics. His original impression that Helen was suffering from tics was immeasurably strengthened, even before the completion of the special tests, by a careful review of her past and present emotional life.

Questioning of Helen's mother revealed that Helen's story was similar in many respects to that of many children who have tics. While the mother was carrying Helen, she followed a rigid self-prescribed schedule of diet, rest and exercise. Everything had to be just so; this dependence upon an inflexible regimen was her way of life. As a baby, Helen was fed the exact types and amounts of food and at the exact times that the mother had read were best for a child. When Helen was learning to walk, her tottering was aggravated by her mother's insistence on early perfection. The same rigid and unreasonable insistence on perfection was directed to the child's bowel- and bladder-training. Helen grew up following her mother's example and desires for perfection to the letter. She knew no other way. But Helen had given in so long and so completely to her mother's unrealistic demands that the thought of asserting herself with anybody at all never could occur to her. Helen had feelings, but she never had been permitted to express them; she had to hold them within herself.

Possibly as a result of this rigid up-bringing, Helen grew up to be a meek child. She became a quiet follower, never a leader. She had little to say and then said it almost apologetically in a half whisper. She was a high-strung child and burst into tears at the slightest provocation. She was very tense and restless and did not fit in well or completely in any group of children. In addition to her shyness, and possibly contributing to this shyness, she was very clumsy in sports. For all these reasons, she generally was frozen out of most group activities. She had withdrawn more and more into herself.

The father was a bully around the house, loudly voicing his opinions and loudly demanding immediate obedience from everybody. He was short-tempered and very impatient with anybody he considered to be sloppy and inefficient. He never had shown any warmth toward his wife or daughter; both of them trembled at his voice or frown. Neither had ever dared to stand up to him. Helen never had been permitted to show

her own feelings or any independence in this household. She
had had to keep everything to herself.

However, the feelings were there, constantly building up
within her and ready to explode in some form under the proper
circumstances. Since she never could be permitted to express
her feelings toward any individual by words or behavior
toward these people, the feelings had to—and did—find their
outlet through her own body. Tics appeared. The incident
with the beach ball, in itself quite trivial, was the needed
incident that caused the tics to appear and that determined
their location. The tics really were caused by the past stormy
relationships with her parents that she was forced to contain
within herself.

If, for some reason, the tics disappeared, the basic problems
remained and continued to ferment; they had to seek an outlet
through other means. After a few months, Helen's tics actually
did go away entirely; itching then appeared all over the body
and always persisted for a few days following any particularly
upsetting emotional experience.

CHAPTER 9

*D*ependency, *T*emper *T*antrums, *B*reath-holding, *F*ainting

Mrs. Smith was married, less because of any warm feelings toward Mr. Smith, but more because it was the "thing to do." When Mr. Smith had an offer of a good job in another city, Mrs. Smith tearfully pleaded with him not to move away from her mother. Mr. Smith, usually very gruff and busy, yielded as was his custom to his wife's tears and pleas.

Perhaps even more than the tears and the pleas, Mr. Smith was influenced by his memory of the last time he was offered a better job in another city. At that time Mrs. Smith agreed that it was a fine opportunity that should not be missed, but kept repeating over and over, "What will Mother do? She'll be all alone. I hate to leave her. She's always so good to us. I don't see how I can get along without her. What will little Eddie do? He's so used to having his grandmother around." The plans were all made. The day before the family expected to move, Mrs. Smith's mother tearfully gave a big farewell party for the family. The next morning, Mrs. Smith awoke with diarrhea, abdominal cramps, breathlessness, cold sweat, racing of the heart, shakiness and snapping pains in the back of the head and the neck. Mrs. Smith was terrified; she insisted that her mother be called immediately to the bedside; she was convinced that she was about to die. After a thorough examination, the physician concluded that all of these complaints were due to acute nervous exhaustion. It was a whole week before Mrs. Smith could get out of bed. During all this time

85

her mother remained at her bedside and ran the household. The planned move was canceled. Hat in hand, Mr. Smith went to his recent employer and asked for his old job back.

The extreme dependency that Mrs. Smith showed toward her mother was evident in little Eddie's feelings toward Mrs. Smith, his mother. Little Eddie had been a very sweet baby who had been very close to his mother from the beginning. Mrs. Smith never could leave him with someone, not even for 5 minutes while she went on an errand, without his raising quite a rumpus. He wanted his Mommy. Even at play, Eddie always had to remain close to his mother. The other children did not like to play with Eddie because he was a "sore loser"; he wanted his own way at play as he was used to having it at home. Mrs. Smith and her husband, big Eddie, often mentioned that they might have trouble getting Eddie to go to school. Their fears were fulfilled. The same problem arose when big Eddie wanted to send his son to summer camp. Mrs. Smith thought it was "terrible for Eddie to go with all those little roughnecks; I know he'd rather stay home." Again, her fears were fulfilled.

The Smiths boasted that Eddie was a perfect son in all respects except one: he always had to have his own way. "I guess that he is just too independent; he wants to assert himself; but that won't be any disadvantage when he grows up." When he did not get his way immediately, Eddie would kick, scream, and scratch his mother and father. In spite of their slapping Eddie back and threatening him with more dire punishment, Eddie's outbursts would not stop until he had had his way.

The forces underneath this extreme dependency of Eddie for his mother were quite unfriendly. Eddie kicked and bit his mother, and she struck back. As overweight Rudy's mother substituted food for love and thereby unwittingly kept Rudy helplessly dependent, Eddie's mother felt that letting Eddie have his own way and keeping him tied to her apron strings was proof of her great love. Her own helpless dependency on her own mother was reflected in her inability to cope with Eddie's rage—biting and kicking—as well as by her response at the same physical level—striking back. Children never should hit their parents. And parents whose relationship with

their children is healthy, need not depend on continuous spankings for discipline. This does not mean that there is not a time
and a place for occasional discipline, but it should be carried
out within a framework of specific and well-understood limits,
recognized by the child, of what he can and must not do. This
does not and never means such utter nonsense that the child
should have permission to do whatever he wishes at all times
under the false but popular notion that this will be best for
the child's developing personality. If the mother and the father
are sure of themselves in managing the child, they will have
little or no difficulty in setting such limits that the child will
obey and about which he will be comfortable. Such limits
should be well understood by the child and should be consistent, applying from day to day and not vacillating with the
mood of the parent. Setting limits makes the child understand
that what is asked is to be done. Empty words accompanied
by feelings which suggest another response by the child are
not setting limits, but to the contrary give tacit permission for
the activity that is being verbally forbidden. For example,
5-year-old Elsie puts her hand in the goldfish bowl. Mother
immediately and automatically says, "No, No!, Elsie, you'll
kill the goldfish, and then we'll have to buy more." As she says
this, the mother smiles indulgently, turns to the father and
audibly whispers, "The little rascal is so cute I can't get angry
with her." This has happened before. Mother says, "No, No!"
but Elsie knows as well as her mother that mother is also
enjoying it. Elsie continues unperturbed.

Except for the baby at the mouth stage who is dependent
upon the mother for food, extreme dependency means that
the person who is dependent is nothing less than a vassal.
How can the vassal in this state of abject humiliation and
practically nonexistent self-esteem love his master? Yet he
needs the master for his support and livelihood. Who could
say that the master who keeps another human being in such a
condition loves the vassal? Such feelings become intensified
when the vassal questions the motives of his master, who in
turn thinks, "Look at all I'm doing for you—the food, the
clothes, the land. You should love me. And I'm giving all this
to you, because I love you." The reader might readily see by

this analogy some of the underlying currents between Eddie and his mother. If the vassal rebels against his master, he immediately loses all the material things he owns and realizes that it is a fight to the death with the master who is stronger. The master realizes that if he does not suppress the vassal's revolt, he, the master, will not be able to live in the style to which he is accustomed. He also has much at stake. By the resulting struggle, each will unleash previously disguised feelings, and each will become aware that their previous amenities and professions of love really hid underlying hatred. The vassal envied his master, and the master had contempt for his slave. This exact situation holds between Eddie and his mother. The tears, the embraces, the clinging and all the other signs of dependency really reveal the fundamental conflict between mother and son. The physical outbursts of anger—the kicking, biting, and the shaking by the shoulders—only serve to bring this underlying conflict to the surface. Each becomes aware that this conflict exists. This only leads to further physical outbursts. The mother and the child attempt to patch up their differences by more fervent protestations of love (and dependency). The mother and the son continue to exist in this state of conflict marked by tears, clinging, and other superficial manifestations of what they consider as "love." They keep their underlying conflict in check by stating that they love each other so much that they cannot leave each other.

Other common problems that occur at the early school period are temper tantrums and breath-holding spells. Four-year-old Sally wants to go out to play. Since she is recovering from a cold her mother wisely feels that she should remain inside, even though the sunny street outside is alive with Sally's playmates. Instead of accepting the wisdom of her mother's decision and doing as other children do under similar circumstances, Sally continues to beg. Mother stands firm. Then suddenly with a loud whoop, Sally is on the floor kicking, screaming and crying uncontrollably: "I want to go out. I want to go out!" Mother immediately runs over and pleads with the child. "Please stop it, Sally—stop it right now—don't bump your head on the floor, you'll only hurt yourself." Her pleas have no effect. Finally, as Sally's tantrum and her mother's alarm increase, the mother says, "Be quiet, Sally, stop it this minute. What will Mrs. Jones next door think. . . . Oh, well, I suppose it won't hurt to go out a little while." The tantrum immediately ceases, and the racking sobs fade away as the screen door slams shut. "You stay in the backyard, Sally. If you don't, you can come right back in. I've got to teach you to obey me."

Most children have had at least one temper tantrum in their lives, but the parents' immediate and correct management has prevented it from recurring. Standing firm in such cases and giving the child a good slap on the behind will show the child that she cannot use that method to get her way. However, Sally has learned from experience that the temper tantrum is a good way to get what she wants. Mother is always alarmed, and if the tantrum continues long enough, her mother will give in. Mother's protestation that "I've got to teach you to obey me," means nothing to Sally when the mother cannot stand firm and back up her words with action. Temper tantrums that continue do so only because they are serving a purpose for the child. The child uses them to get her way. When the child stops getting what she wants by having a tantrum, the tantrums will cease. In the temper tantrum, the important question is not the remedy but what is at fault in the emotional relationship between parent and child that accounts for the tantrum.

Actually, another form of temper tantrum but occurring in younger children and more frightening to the mother and the father is breath-holding. The child cannot get her way and cries so violently that she holds her breath, and consequently the skin turns blue. Sometimes the child will actually pass out. Usually the combination of the child's turning blue and then passing out understandably alarms the parents—so much so that they give in, and the child gets what she wanted. The worried parents send out an urgent call for the physician. There is no medicine for breath-holding spells. The child's physical health is good, and such episodes will not harm the child physically. There is only one answer: show the child that she cannot use this method to get her way.

Both breath-holding spells and temper tantrums can be prevented by parental firmness. Once established, however, the habit is difficult to break. Education of the parents in situations such as these is as important as education of the child.

Fainting in children is a difficult problem. The physician knows that there are numerous causes for fainting, some of which are more serious than others. Only he can determine the nature of the fainting by many careful studies that might include x-ray pictures, spinal fluid examinations and brain-wave studies. Fainting can be a manifestation of epilepsy, brain tumor, low blood sugar and many other diseases of the brain and of other parts of the body. Fainting can also be an expression of extreme terror. Thus, everyone knows of the child (or the adult) who passes out prior to receiving an injection or upon hearing some bad news. This is one way in which the child can be protected from feeling all the unpleasantness associated with what is anticipated or what is happening around him.

CHAPTER 10

Bed-wetting, Sleep-walking, Sleep-talking

Like soiling, bed-wetting is very rarely due to factors other than emotional. In the overwhelming number of cases of bed-wetting, an emotional conflict between parent and child is the cause.

The punishment did not work. Mrs. Y. made 8-year-old Francis make his own bed and wash the sheets whenever he wet the bed, but the bed-wetting continued. Other unsuccessful home remedies included: no liquids after supper, making sure that he urinated before going to bed, and using the alarm clock to awaken both mother and child at 2:00 A.M. so he would urinate. Finally, more in embarrassment than in desperation, Mrs. Y. and Francis appeared at their physician's office. "Doctor, I've tried everything, but Francis still wets the bed at night. What's wrong?" The physician did a complete physical examination, as was his routine when he saw a new patient, and also examined Francis' urine. Everything was normal. Suspecting where the trouble was, from his years of experience with this particular family as well as from his previous experiences with similar problems, he asked to see Mrs. Y. alone.

"Doctor, we had not expected that Francis would come as soon as he did. We were not ready. We wanted to establish our home first. He was a lot of trouble. It isn't that I haven't given him enough attention, Doctor. My husband and I never even went out until he was 18 months old. Even then, we worried about the baby-sitter and phoned home every hour.

We gave him more toys than any other child in the neighbor-hood. All in all, he's been a good son to us, never getting into trouble like other boys, quiet, likes to stay around the house and gets into no fights. I guess he's a mama's boy! He always wants to sit on my lap and kiss me. And Francis' Daddy is so very proud of him. He's already dreaming of Francis' win-ning a letter in college and then taking over the family business."

The physician, knowing the importance of certain aspects of bed-wetting, then probed further into this situation.

"Yes, he still sleeps in the same bedroom with us. I don't know why you ask about that. We have never given it any thought. Francis used to be afraid of the dark so we had him sleep with us. And I guess we never changed. As a matter of fact, he often sleeps with me when his father's away. We're very close. We keep our other bedroom as a guest room for my father and mother. . . . I still don't see why you ask that. Francis is asleep by the time we get to bed and he sleeps like a log.

"Of course we do. We're not prissy at our house. I can't see why you make such a fuss about dressing and undressing in front of children. There's nothing to be ashamed of in the human body. And it is only when you try to hide the body and be a prude that you stimulate the child's interest. Francis has seen me many times, so I suppose he knows about the differences between boys and girls."

This unnaturally close relationship between mother and son described by Mrs. Y. is often seen with numerous variations in cases of bed-wetting in boys. Francis, who slept in the same room with his parents, could not help but be aware of the physical aspects of marriage. It would be naive to assume that he was that heavy a sleeper. Furthermore, seeing his mother and father so very close to each other in a way he cannot understand is confusing. How could she give herself to the father this way? This very upsetting situation that should not exist, further intensifies the current rivalry with his father. It can be seen how the boy might well be angry with his father and wish to hurt him, or even to get rid of him altogether. "If Daddy were gone, I'd have Mommy all to myself." Such wishes are very frightening to a small boy when he realizes how big and strong his father is.

While the parents believe that the child is fast asleep, he actually lies in the borderland of dreams and reality, where wishes can become true and where the events that go on around him may become twisted to conform to his desires. Fact, fantasy, desire and half-knowledge all become hopelessly muddled in his mind. As many parents know who have watched children of this age play, the world of make-believe is very real to them: making sure the dolly is warm enough, feeding the Teddy bear, having fun with imaginary playmates and fear of the boogie-man. Fantasy can become confused with fact.

"If Daddy were gone, I'd have Mommy all to myself." Sleeping in the same room with his parents, then, Francis may fancy that his wishes against his rival are being realized; he may easily become convinced that his mother is really hurting his father. But, the situation boomerangs for little Francis. "If Mommy can do this to Daddy, why can't she do this to me?" One can understand the confused mixture of love, hate, fear and futile hope as this boy sleeps with his mother during his father's absence. This fear finds some support in fact when Francis has such recent memories of the conflict over bowel-training. He remembers how his mother behaved. "If you do not have a bowel movement when I ask you to, I can't love you." Francis also senses that his mother's "love," that her staying at home with him, never letting him out of her sight, her overprotection and all her gifts of toys are not manifestations of genuine affection (see Chap. 9). The physician knew that Francis' unplanned arrival was a hardship on the mother and the father from the mother's point of view. He also learned other facts about the mother's own past and her own growing up. He knew that the unplanned arrival of a baby is no more than temporarily upsetting in a healthy household. But in this mother's case, as a result of an emotionally sick growing-up period (of the type already alluded to in this book), the physician knew that Francis' mother would have problems with her own children, planned or unplanned.

With reason to doubt his mother's love and with his fear of her, Francis entered the lion's den when he slept in his parents' bedroom. "Mommy can do this to Daddy; why can't she do this to me?" Francis' solution to this terrifying problem was to make a complete about-face. He would be as unlike his Daddy as he could be. He would do nothing to provoke his mother. He would be timid, quiet and completely obedient to her. He could not be masculine at all, because then he would receive the same hurt that he fancied his father received from the mother. If the frightened Francis were to have shown his true feelings of resentment and rage at his mother, he would hardly have stood a chance in the ensuing conflict. It was easier to remain the quiet, conforming, submissive boy, the mama's boy. But, as in previous examples, the pent-up feelings and tension must escape in some manner. In Francis' case, it had to escape in a manner acceptable to the mother and in keeping with his submissiveness.

It has already been noted (see Chap. 3) that Francis entered the first romance stage (when these problems of self-identification as a male first came to the fore) shortly after he was bladder-trained. In a boy such as Francis with a strong-willed mother, bladder-training would have presented another occasion for the mother to impress her dominance indelibly on her son. This uneven conflict would cause tension to build up in Francis as he was forced to submit without apparent protest.

As a result of Francis' submissiveness to his mother and his mistaken fancies of the meaning of the husband-wife relationship, Francis was confused between active masculinity (which he was afraid to recognize in himself) and passive femininity. There are boys in rebellion against the significant people in their environment, who discharge their pent-up tensions by fighting with others, shouting and doing that which is expressly forbidden by parents and others in authority. Sometimes such boys may even wet themselves in the daytime as another act of rebellion of which they are fully aware. However, a passive boy such as Francis would be incapable of rebelling so flagrantly lest his true underlying rage (see Chap. 5) become unleashed and overwhelm him and those about him. But tension must escape. In a boy such as Francis, it could do so only through the lines along which his personality had been molded by his parents. Thus he can rebel in a passive (effeminate) way by bed-wetting at night in the borderland between dream and reality, fact, fantasy and desire. It is only in this borderland that such a boy could find refuge from the many subtle tyrannies which are perpetrated upon his developing personality. Interestingly enough, he uses, as the means for the release of such tension, that part of his anatomy which most differentiates him from a female.

It may also be noted that it is not unusual for healthy children to masturbate sometime in their lives (see p. 45); in contrast, such behavior is unusual in children who wet the bed. This failure again reveals the fear that such boys have in admitting their masculinity. Masturbation would arouse uncomfortable and dangerous feelings by directing the boy's attention to the genitals.

In girls, the fundamental causes of bed-wetting are similar to those described for boys; however, there are a few twists peculiar to the sex. One difference is that there are fewer bed-wetters among girls than among boys. However, the fundamental problem in girls is also frequently an emotional conflict stemming from the girl's sleeping in the same bedroom with her parents; but in the girl's case, it is her father who is unnaturally close to her. She has fantasies analogous to those of the boy; but the twist is that she competes with her mother for her father. Her wish to have her father for herself and to have her mother out of the picture is intensified by watching her father behave toward her mother in a way she cannot understand. She mistakenly believes that her father is hurting her mother.

For example, 12-year-old Clara's previous relationship with her father had been unnaturally close. He continued to dangle her on his knee, tickle her and walk into the bathroom to scrub her back (ostensibly to help her clean herself). Clara and her father were in the habit of dashing unannounced in and out of each other's bedroom while the other was dressing. "There is no false modesty in this house!" While carrying on so consistently with 12-year-old Clara in this apparently cozy and cuddly manner, the father was in many other ways blatantly inconsistent. His promises to Clara meant little or nothing. The promised trip to the zoo with Clara was peremptorily replaced by a golf date without explanation or apology. Clara peered over her father's newspaper and was sent to her room for the evening as punishment. Inconsistency, unfair punishment, or the ignoring of Clara when it suited his whim, revealed the father's true feelings toward her. Again, from what has been shown previously in this book, such a father who shows "love" in the ways described does not really love. Furthermore, even if the father had remained consistent in his unwarranted demonstrations of unnatural love, such unwholesome actions could hardly be called love when the effect is, in so many similar cases, ruinous to the girl. This has been shown and will be further illustrated by the many examples in this book.

From deep-seated emotional problems derived from his own growing-up period, this father had many deep-rooted problems with women: his mother, sister, teacher, wife and daughter. During the daughter's first romance period, seeds sown in previous generations bore fruit. The father's problems stemming from his own first romance period remained unsolved and blazed furiously in the daughter during her first romance period as the home situation fed the flames.

Returning to Clara's fear that her father was hurting her mother, Clara, like the boy, confused fact with fantasy. She, being small and weak, could not get rid of her mother and have her father all for herself. In the excitement of the marital relationship, Clara was jerked from her half sleep in which fact, fantasy and desire were merged confusingly together. In her state of highly charged emotions, she mistakenly believed that her father was hurting her mother. Sensing her father's true feelings toward her, Clara was then afraid that he could do the same thing to her that he had done to Mother. Her solution was to act differently from Mother, to deny her femininity. If she were to act like her father, no man would hurt her. Therefore, she acted like a tomboy: she became bossy, domineering, a leader, an athlete, a competitor with boys (and later men) in their own fields. There are many variations, but this unnatural closeness of daughter to father (analogous to the unnatural relationship already described for son and mother) is the basic theme so often seen in girls who wet the bed.

As in boys who wet their beds, masturbation is seldom seen in girls who wet their beds. The reason for its frequent absence is the same as in the case of the boys. The girl who wets the bed is afraid to masturbate. That would make her perilously aware of her femininity in body and feelings and therefore vulnerable to her father (and other men).

The situations described reveal the causes of many of the cases of bed-wetting. Boys with this problem appear feminine in feeling and behavior; the girls appear masculine in feeling and behavior. This is true even though the boy may look big, strong and masculine, and the girl may look small, dainty and feminine. It is not the body build or shape but the accompanying feelings and behavior that determine how successfully the boy grows up to be a real man and the girl grows up to be a real woman. Fundamentally, the problem in boys is too much passivity while in girls the problem is one of protest against the feminine role associated with their sex in our culture. It is clear that bed-wetting, like obesity or asthma, for example, is only one symptom seen in the emotionally disturbed child. Most bed-wetters have or have had other evidences of their emotional problems: nightmares, temper tantrums, nail-biting, eating problems, soiling and delinquency.

Many questions on the causes of this type of bed-wetting have yet to be answered. It is understandable that to some readers the concepts so far presented in this book may be unbelievable and even difficult to accept. However, if such patients and their parents are studied carefully and treated over many many hours by collaborative technic (see Introduction), the validity of these concepts slowly becomes apparent.

There are cases of bed-wetting due to factors other than those already described. Bed-wetting often occurs when a child is sick or has just been hospitalized and therefore has become temporarily and understandably disturbed emotionally. This symptom is also seen frequently in the young child

(usually the first child) when a baby brother or sister is born (see p. 27). In such circumstances, the bed-wetting is not at all uncommon, and the parents usually show no alarm, especially since the symptom shortly disappears of its own accord. Children who are deprived of any genuine close relationship with an adult to whom they always can turn for help and advice may be bed-wetters. Such children, as a result of this extreme deprivation, may be emotionally retarded (so that they continue to function at an emotional level earlier than is consistent with their ages) and even intellectually backward (see Chap. 19). Bed-wetting due to this cause is one of the commoner emotional disturbances occurring in some institutions for children (for example, certain orphanages).

The rarest causes of bed-wetting are those due to certain specific abnormalities of the urinary tract or the nerves which stimulate it. Epilepsy may be another cause for wetting the bed at night. Finally, bed-wetting may be associated with some severe degrees of mental deficiency.

In any event, only the physician can determine the cause for the child's wetting the bed at night.

Walking and talking while apparently still asleep are further good examples of how feelings can be expressed through physical activity without the child's being aware of what he is doing.

The child may walk in his sleep to his parents' bedroom, which he associates with love; the bathroom, which he associates with other biologically indispensable urges; or the kitchen, which he associates with food. This remarkable feat usually is performed without the child's hurting himself. This is an excellent illustration of how indelibly imprinted on the child's mind memories can be and how they can be used to determine the child's actions without his being aware of the action or the processes of thought which guided the action. The next morning he cannot even remember the episode. He might even be totally flabbergasted if his parents were to ask him about it.

This remarkable demonstration shows how, in health, the child's memories can direct him to satisfy his basic cravings (for love, food and elimination) without his even being aware that he acted in that manner or that he even used the memory. But, the memory was there, and the memory was used. The principles seen in health in this manner are fully applicable to disease where the basic cravings and feelings, distorted though they may be, must also find an outlet. This automatic nonvolitional use of memory to determine current feelings and actions goes on all the time in everybody, child and adult, in sleep (with dreams) and in wakefulness.

Sleep-walking usually disappears gradually as the child grows older and begins to face his problems and satisfy his needs realistically in the world of wakefulness. If the sleep-walking persists, the child should be seen by a physician. The child's deep-seated feelings may well be disturbed, usually from a disturbed parent-child relationship, and these feelings may be seeking an outlet through such behavior. It is less threatening to admit to certain cravings, needs and feelings during sleep than during wakefulness, especially when such cravings, needs and feelings are forbidden satisfaction and when their existence cannot even be admitted during wakefulness. Society and parents do not hold the child responsible for what happens during sleep.

The same general principles that hold for sleep-walking also apply to sleep-talking.

CHAPTER 11

The Boy Who Was Afraid to Go to School

Five-year-old Mike enthusiastically looked forward to starting kindergarten. As the great day dawned, Mike was up early, ate a good breakfast and, with some impatience, waited for his mother to get ready to take him to school. "Hurry up, Mommy, we'll be late!" When they arrived at school, however, some changes had occurred. Mike was staring at all the other children moving about, had little to say and then began sucking his thumb. Finally, when his mother introduced him to Miss Jones, his teacher, it was more than Mike could stand. Although Miss Jones was a young, friendly, smiling, lady like Mommy, she was not Mommy. Mike held tightly to his mother's hand. As she tried to leave, the storm broke: he cried, held tightly to her and could not even speak. His mother was sympathetic and kneeled down to speak to him as Mike held on. "This is really very scary for you Mikie, I know. It's no fun to meet all these strange boys and girls at one time. But you are growing up, Mikie, and all big boys and girls go to school. Even though we talked about going to school before, I know you don't like the idea that Mommy is going to leave you. But you know it is just for this morning and I'll be back when it's time to eat. And then we can talk about what you and all your new friends did. Miss Jones, your teacher knows how little boys feel at this time. They don't like their Mommies to leave them and are even a little bit mad with their Mommies. But Mommies and teachers understand, Mikie. Miss Jones has lots of games, and I know it will be lots of fun." At this point Miss Jones sympathetically took hold of Mike's hand and gently pulled him to her as his mother just as gently but firmly disengaged herself, kissed him and left. "Good-bye Mikie," she smiled, "I'll see you soon."

Charlie U. also had looked forward to school as he spoke about it boastingly to his playmates. At school that morning, to the casual observer, there was very little difference between Charlie and Mikie. Charlie clung to his mother, sucked his thumb, and then suddenly began to scream and howl. No words came, just loud piercing, unintelligible screams. Charlie kicked at his mother and Miss Jones, who had been unable to say anything yet. Mrs. U., tears in her own eyes, cradled her boy in her arms as she sat on a small kindergarten chair. She cooed, "It's alright, little Charlie. Don't cry. Teacher won't hurt you. Mommy wouldn't let anyone hurt you. Please Charlie, please be a good little boy. When Mommy comes back, if you've been a good boy, we'll go together, you and I, and have an ice cream cone. Just you and I, no teacher and no daddy."

Charlie held on to his mother tenaciously. "No, no!, Don't leave me, Mommy. Please, Mommy! Don't leave me!" During this pandemonium, Mrs. U. looked around the room, saw the clock on the wall and knew that it was time to leave Charlie with Miss Jones. Charlie would have none of this. Crying, sobbing and clinging, he blindly kicked, striking his mother's shins with his shoe. "No son of mine is going to hit me!" Mrs. U.'s eyes blazed as she grasped Charlie by both shoulders, shook him violently and struck him on the cheek with the back of her open hand. "I've got to teach you to stop hitting and biting me." Angrily shaking her finger and with her voice trembling, she continued brokenly, "Little boys who love their Mommies don't do things like that. You're acting just like a baby. You'd better be good to Miss Jones, because she'll tell me everything that happens, and when you're bad, I'll know it. You can't do in school what you do at home. You can't bite and kick other people like you do Mommy."

Apparently noticing the other mothers in the classroom for the first time, Mrs. U. said, "Charlie's never been away from home before, and this is hard on both of us." Mrs. U. got up and walked to the door, turned and looked at Charlie struggling and crying in Miss Jones' arms, and then impulsively ran back to her son. Tears in her eyes, Mrs. U. embraced Charlie, kissed him and said, "If Mommy is a little late today, Charlie, don't worry; just stay with your teacher until I come."

Mrs. U. left. Charlie and Mike were both crying. Miss Jones was not unduly concerned about Mike, but she knew that Charlie faced a real problem.

After 3 days, Mike looked forward to school and the games with his classmates and teacher. In fact, when he and his mother arrived at the classroom, he would immediately leave her and eagerly run into the room, yelling to some classmate who had arrived earlier. The tears and the fears of the first day were gone.

Mike was indeed growing up. He always had received love from his mother and gave love in return. Long ago he had learned to trust his mother's word. She meant what she said and always did what she promised to do. When she promised that she would return, she was specific. " . . . I'll be back when it's time to eat." From past experience, Mike believed her. Although only 5 years old, and beginning kindergarten, Mike already had a good measure of self-reliance. His mother and father were straightforward in expressing their feelings for Mike as well as in showing each other mutual love and respect. They had no warped need to keep Mike too closely tied to themselves. Mike was able to test many things for himself and even looked forward to new situations like school. Of course he cried; he was faced with a completely new situation with strange people. But Mike's faith in his mother and his own curiosity and fledgling independence were able to overcome quickly this initial fear. Mike soon settled into his new surroundings. Mike's mother understood and respected his feelings even to the point of admitting to him that he might be mad at her and frightened. By putting herself in his shoes and being able to accept his justified anger, Mike's mother permitted him to express himself. It was evident that Mike did not strike his mother. That never had been permitted and never would be. Mike had expressed his rage in response to a justifiable situation. His rage was specific and directed at his mother. It was realistic in so far as it was accepted by the mother, and limits were set to the expression of his rage. He could cry or say he was angry with his

mother, but he could not resort to striking his mother or engage in any destructive acts. The rage did not get out of hand
and, since the underlying feelings between mother and son
were sound, there was no need to disguise their feelings by
meaningless words and gestures purported to show "love."

Miss Jones's hunch about Charlie was correct. Charlie was
unable to live and play happily while remaining separated from
his mother. The original scene on the first day of school was
repeated daily with many variations. Charlie never really accepted his playmates—nor they him. As a matter of fact, Miss
Jones was called to the office of the principal, Mr. Penrod, a
number of times. Already having met Mrs. U. himself, Mr. Penrod understood much of the situation and sympathized with
Charlie and Miss Jones. "Charlie is really tied to his mother's
apron strings, isn't he? Mrs. U. even had her family doctor
phone me. He is well acquainted with the situation and has
often tried to persuade Mrs. U. to take Charlie to the Child
Guidance Center to see what can be done. As you might guess,
Charlie had been having many problems long before school
began. But Mrs. U. only gets angry with the doctor and denies
that any emotional problem exists. Here we have all this interest nowadays in mental hygiene . . . raising funds, setting up
centers for study, magazine articles . . . but it seems that those
who need help the most, will not go. They just come in and
complain to us. It's always our fault . . . the teachers. We're
expected to teach these kids what they should have learned at
home. There are certain responsibilities which are the parent's
. . . not the teacher's. It seems that we must have one or two
pupils like Charlie every year. Poor Charlie! He has a hard
road ahead. Well, Miss Jones, let's do what we can for Charlie."

Mr. Penrod really defined Charlie's problem when he said
that Charlie was tied to his mother's apron strings. Like the
problem of Rudy, the obese boy, this problem is really one of
too much dependency upon the parents. When Mr. Penrod
stated that Charlie's problem began before school, although
the mother was now blaming the school as the cause, he did
not realize how long before school the problem really first
appeared. Charlie was an unexpected and unplanned pregnancy. His mother and father had wanted to wait for a few

years while they were both working in their new florist shop. Charlie was a feeding problem, sucked his thumb, still bit his nails and still occasionally wet the bed. Mr. and Mrs. U. felt that if Charlie had not appeared so inopportunely, both would have been in better financial condition than they were. Beneath this reasoning were some facts that were not discussed.

As in the case of Rudy's mother, it was impossible for Mrs. U. to see any connection between Charlie's current problems and the past feelings and experiences in her own life. Mrs. U.'s father was a very strong-willed individual, a virtual dictator in his household. Mrs. U.'s mother was a very timid little woman with many fears and superstitions. Charlie's mother was raised in this unwholesome and unrealistic atmosphere. Mrs. U., as a girl, thus lived in the constant fear (and hatred) of her father's tyranny and the interminable harping of her mother. "Don't touch this and don't do that." The fears of Mrs. U.'s mother served as an escape valve for her own tension resulting from her unhealthy relationship with her husband (Mrs. U.'s father). It would be hard to imagine her as having any warm feelings for a man who was so aloof and stern with his wife and daughter. Consequently, Mrs. U. and her mother depended upon each other; each fed the fears of the other. Neither was really happy; neither could exist without the other. Even when Mrs. U. went to Girl Scout Camp one summer, she was very homesick, and the camp physician had to send for her mother. Mrs. U.'s extreme dependency upon her mother was carried forward another generation to her son in Charlie's extreme dependence upon her. In each person, Mrs. U.'s mother, Mrs. U. herself and Mrs. U.'s son, Charlie, this extreme dependence was manifested by the exaggerated fears of being separated one from the other.

In practically all instances of school phobia, the problems are, with many variations, similar to those of Charlie. The extreme anxiety resulting from any separation between a child (or grown-up) and another individual has the same basis in helpless dependency and mutal hatred as in the analogy of master and slave presented previously (see p. 87).

CHAPTER 12

Asthma and the Emotions

Dr. M. was coming out of Grandma L.'s room. This time she was complaining of a "lump" stuck in the throat so that she could not swallow. Dr. M. had been seeing Mrs. L. since he first began practice 30 years previously. His office record on her was a voluminous one and contained, over the years, practically all the examinations and tests known to medical science. All these studies had been normal. Yet new complaints continued to crop up. Dr. M. knew that Mrs. L.'s troubles were due to nervous tension and not the cancer she often feared. Dr. M.'s suggestions that Mrs. L. see a "nerve specialist" always met with angry refusals. When Dr. M. discussed the problem informally with Dr. O., a psychiatrist, at the hospital coffee shop, Dr. O. threw up his hands and said, "Bill, I can understand how you feel. It's just one of those cases that can use psychiatric help but can't see it. You'll just have to carry along as you have done. After all, she might be like the little boy who cried, "Wolf." You can never tell. She might really develop cancer some day. That has happened to me a few times. You'll just have to watch her and check each new complaint."

As Dr. M. mulled over these thoughts, he passed an open door in the hallway outside Grandma's room. He accidentally saw her married daughter, Adele, who was playfully wrestling on the bed with her 11-year-old son, Thomas. Giggling and laughing, they rolled over and over on the bed, their arms tightly clasped around each other, and Thomas trying to get a scissors hold on his mother with his legs. Neither, of course, noticed Dr. M., who shrugged his shoulders, grunted and walked out of the house, slamming the front door. As Dr. M.

drove down the street, his thoughts returned to Thomas and
his mother, Adele.

"Here it is again. Adele is just like her mother. It's like talking to the wind: Adele, is it still necessary for you to bathe
Thomas? Why haven't you moved his bed out of your own
bedroom so he does not sleep in the same room with you and
your husband? Why must you walk Thomas to school each
morning? And now this wrestling match! And why call him
Thomas? Why not Tom or Tommy?

"It's hard to believe that Thomas is already 11 years old.
With all the boys his own age in the neighborhood, why must he
continue playing with the 6- and 8-year-olds? Adele seems to
do everything possible to keep him young. I wonder what
Adele gets out of it? How pathetic it all is when he has one of
his asthma attacks: Thomas in bed wheezing, puffing and
gasping for air; the room reeking with vapors and menthol;
Adele half lying on the bed with her son, hugging him to herself, kissing him and repeating, 'My poor little Thomas; Mommy
will take care of you.' Thomas clenching his mother with both
arms as if she were his lifeline, refusing to let her go. 'Hold me,
Mommy, please don't leave me; I'm afraid.' And Nelson (the
father), standing in the doorway looking helplessly on; he
never says anything; he never does anything.

"What a surprise it was that last time. Adele using a sup-
pository on Thomas in front of Grandma, Uncle, Father and
myself. 'Why have you never used suppositories on Thomas,
Doctor? That other young doctor prescribed them when you
were away last summer. Thomas likes them, and they help
more than the medicines you gave by mouth'."

Dr. M. mused, "Suppositories! Perhaps for another child,
but not for Thomas! Can't blame Dr. Y.; he didn't know Thomas
or his family.

"During the attacks, Adele tends to Thomas' every whim.
What mother wouldn't when her child is having so much
trouble breathing? But there was that time when Thomas was
out playing in the yard and Adele was calling from her back
door. 'Thomas, get off that ladder! Get off right now! You'll
hurt yourself. Thomas, listen to me!' No response from Thomas
who continued his play unconcernedly. 'Oh hell; fall off and

break your neck. I don't care.' And Adele returned into the house and went back to her television and coffee."

Dr. M. knew that Thomas had numerous allergies to house dust and many pollens as proved by skin tests. He recalled that Grandma L.'s husband, Thomas' grandfather, had had asthma all his life and then died at 80 years of age in an auto accident. Dr. M. knew that in Thomas' case, as in many instances of asthma, there was an interplay of emotional and allergic factors causing the asthma. Of course, there are also cases of asthma in which the emotional factor is the only cause, and there are also cases of asthma in which the allergic factor is the only cause. Dr. M. also recognized that many cases of asthma are so frightening to the child and his parents that the child can become secondarily disturbed emotionally as a result of the asthma. But this can occur with any prolonged or severe illness in any individual, child or adult. In Thomas, however, the emotional problems were one of the causes (in addition to the known allergies) and not the effects of the asthma.

Thomas' case was in many ways similar to the problem of Mike, the boy with the fear of going to school. Thomas was too close to his mother, too dependent upon her.

Thomas had been a very well-behaved baby. In fact, he rarely cried. His mother "broke him" of the thumb-sucking habit very early. There was no nail-biting, ear-pulling or head-banging. Thomas was a very obedient child—or was this only what the mother called obedience? Certainly in the example above two things were clear: Thomas ignored his mother's command and continued to climb the ladder anyhow. His mother was the same way: she told Thomas not to climb the ladder, but then was not only incapable of putting meaning into her words but also revealed her own feelings by saying, "Oh hell; fall off and break your neck."

A few words about Adele. She had been bent on becoming a career woman until she married Nelson when both were 36 years old. She never had been greatly interested in marrying, because, as she said, "Marriage is not what people say it is. Father was never home. He was always on the road as a salesman. How I'd look forward to his coming home! He'd always have a real surprise for me on my birthday. Poor Mother . . .

staying home all the time and taking care of me. With all her suffering, she never complained. Poor Mother . . . sick as long as I can remember."

Dr. M., the man who knew the family best, was sympathetic with Adele. He knew that at the time little girls are developing their later attitudes toward men through their relationship with their father, Adele in fact had had no father. To Adele, a father was an individual who came home on rare occasions (like her birthday) for short periods of time and gave her presents. He never showed any truly fatherly interest in his daughter. How many times are gifts and other material things given as substitutes for love? Adele had a roomful of toys but no father. Aware of this, although not necessarily able to put it into words, Adele resented it. Her feelings and her emptiness colored her later attitudes toward men. She was left at home with a mother who often said, "I have been more fortunate than most women in marriage. Henry is a wonderful provider." At heart, Adele's mother knew that the satisfaction of material needs could not undo the harm from the emotional vacuum in which she lived. These needs as well as more basic needs stemming from her own childhood could not be recognized as such but masqueraded as innumerable physical complaints and fears. As a little girl, Adele greatly missed her father, and she vaguely wondered if her mother's illnesses were not also due to her father's repeated absences. Adele's mother had a marriage in name only. No one cared for her, aside from Dr. M.'s predecessor who was busy even then with her many illnesses. Mrs. L. could not give of herself to Adele; she could only give countless toys, dresses, candy and "everything a child would want." Not having received love, she was unable to give any. To Mrs. L., this giving of gifts and supplying material wants meant being a good mother. Nobody cared for Adele as a person. No wonder Dr. M. felt so sorry for her as a child and later as a woman. What in later life could ever satisfy these early unsatisfied needs? In her adolescent dreams, Adele cherished the hope that a husband and a baby would give her what she never had had. She also received the advice that her mother had received earlier from many well-meaning friends and counselors, "What you need is to get married."

As a young career woman, Adele met many stable, rising young men, but she was not interested in any of them. Then, when she was 30 years old, she met Nelson. "He was such a good companion." Their courtship lasted for 6 years, and finally, one day, Adele's mother said, "You're getting older now, Adele, and Nelson is an awfully nice fellow. Why don't you get married? If you cannot find a house, you can live with me. Every girl should get married."

Nelson is a nonentity. He works, earns money and helps around the house by making beds, scrubbing floors, doing laundry and occasionally preparing meals. Adele achieved her goal. She has a "model husband" who likes to stay around the house and is always at home. "The situation is so different from Mother's!"

How does all this background information tie in with Thomas' asthma? What do all these life experiences of his grandmother, mother and father mean to Thomas? Dr. M. was aware that most of Thomas' attacks of asthma followed situations which conformed to a definite pattern. With careful study of what was happening to Thomas and his family just prior to an attack, Dr. M. could usually find this pattern. Thomas' attacks occurred at any time of the year; therefore, they were due to something which did not vary with the pollen seasons. These attacks usually followed a situation in which Thomas was faced with a separation or threat of separation or in which overtones of the "first romance" were being handled in an unhealthy seductive manner. Thus, during the previous year alone, Dr. M. had been called to treat Thomas following a fishing trip with his father; the day his mother was hospitalized for a minor illness; and the day after accompanying his father and the family dog on a squirrel hunt. The most recent attack of asthma was the most interesting and graphic of all. Adele predicted it would occur, "Thomas has never been to camp before—has never even been away from home before. I know if I send him to camp, he'll have one of his attacks." He went to camp; he had an attack; he returned home in 2 days.

For a child as dependent as Thomas and with all the negative feelings that such a state really implies (see p. 87), one of the most frightening things that could happen is separation or threat of separation from the mother. At the price of submission to every whim and wish of his mother, Thomas receives "love": food, a roof over his head, clothes and toys. Submission also means the absolute denial of any angry feelings. Like Grandma, Thomas always smiles. Other children may cry but not Thomas. Adele defines her love in terms of worldly goods for Thomas and she defines Thomas' love of her in terms of the complete dependence of Thomas upon her. Nelson is a good provider; he therefore loves. To show her great "love" to Thomas, to herself and to the world, Adele is extremely generous to Thomas. In fact, she boasts of this and repeatedly compares herself with her neighbor, Mrs. Brown, "She has 5 kids ... all dressed in rags. They'll never have a college education. I can't see how that family can always be so happy. They have nothing." Adele's relationship with Thomas lacks only one important ingredient: mutual, genuine affection and respect.

In such a state of complete helplessness, Thomas is all bottled up in a nearly hopeless predicament. Thomas' mother would never tolerate any signs of independence or rebellion. Thomas cannot be permitted even to cry. In children (as in adults), strong angry feelings directed toward someone almost always arouse fears of receiving similar feelings in return. Thomas' rage toward his mother leads to a fear of receiving the same feelings from his mother but with one catch: mother is bigger, stronger and older, and Thomas is dependent upon her. Understandably, Thomas is very unhappy and even angry about being kept in such a helpless condition by his mother. Thomas has two choices. He can give vent to his rage, in which case he would lose everything, even the warped semblance of love that he still receives from his mother. The second choice is to show no independence or rebellion but to swallow his indignation and appear entirely docile to all outward appearances. But the rage persists, builds up and must finally escape in some manner. When it does escape, it still cannot be shown against the mother who really evokes the anger. It must escape through an acceptable channel. In Thomas' case, it cannot be directed against people (whom he fears); it can be directed only against himself, his own body. Asthma appears.

In other conditions, the causes vary, and some are understood better than others. What is known, though, is that Thomas' attacks were triggered by definite situations and events in his life in which his dependent relationship upon his mother was threatened. The solution was based on Thomas' approach to life. During the attacks, Thomas became totally dependent. His mother treated him like a baby. The relationship of mutual dependence between mother and child under which Thomas and his mother lived was re-established and strengthened. A reconciliation was effected, and the asthma attack went away.

There was another aggravating factor bearing on Thomas' asthma. At 11 years of age, not only were the problems of the "first romance" unsettled but, as a result of his relationship to his parents, Thomas was badly confused. He felt uncertain about his role as a young boy soon to enter manhood (see Chap. 10). Thomas still slept in the same room with his parents. His problem was even more difficult, because his mother, Adele, was so unnaturally close to him. The early feelings of competition with his father for his mother's affection persisted. Whenever Thomas was separated from his mother and placed in a competitive situation with his father, he had attacks of asthma. Hunting and fishing with his father, situations with potential dangers (i.e., use of firearms, boating in deep waters), precipitated attacks of asthma. Similarly, Adele's hospitalization, with the implied danger to her life and health, precipitated an attack.

Thomas was hopelessly confused in his role as a boy and son for still other reasons. As you will remember, Thomas' mother was the boss in this family. Nelson, the father, did the housework. Since the father was confused concerning his role as a man, Thomas, who would imitate his father, was similarly confused. Although Adele's feelings and behavior as a mother were bizarre, they did follow a definite pattern which would provide a definite formulation, even if faulty, for Thomas' own feelings and behavior toward her (and other women in later life). Nelson, the father, occupied a subordinate position. In contrast with Adele's own strong feelings and behavior, those of Nelson were pale, drab, lifeless and without substance. By Nelson's inability to accept his role as a father and a man, Thomas was delivered into the hands of his mother. Thomas, like all boys, had a normal healthy tendency to imitate his father. But how could he imitate a vacuum?

Nervous eczema or neurodermatitis is closely related to asthma. Both the nervous eczema and the asthma frequently occur together at the same time or at different times in the same child. Both have many emotional and allergic factors. In some cases one factor may be more important than the other. The physician frequently sees acute attacks of nervous eczema with an itchy, oozing, red rash which appears all over the body after a particularly upsetting emotional situation. Such children are on the surface often very co-operative and polite. They usually have great difficulty in expressing any anger toward people. They are afraid to voice or show any anger. But the anger which these children have from their own highly disturbed relationships with their parents in addition to the anger resulting from the usual day-to-day life experiences must seek an outlet. However, they can express their anger against themselves, through their own bodies. Following disturbing imbroglios with their parents or other people, these children start scratching all over their bodies, and the skin becomes fiery red. The more red the skin becomes, the more it itches; the more it itches, the more the child scratches. It is a self-perpetuating cycle initiated and fed by emotional turmoil. In many cases of nervous eczema, parent-child emotional maladjustments similar to those already described for nervous asthma are present.

CHAPTER 13

Specific Causes for Delinquency

"Teen-age gangs terrorize neighborhood." "Fifty-thousand dollars damage done to school by young vandals." "Comic books blamed for delinquency." "Twelve-year-old held for fatal shooting." "Knife victim identifies youth as assailant." "Girls held on morals charge." "Youth nabbed for fire-setting." "Youth held for Main Street robbery." "Mother pleads for son: 'He never had a chance.'"

These assorted newspaper headlines and the interest shown by the wide variety of groups working with the problem of delinquency make it quite clear that there are many factors other than emotional contributing to this problem. For instance, in certain neighborhoods there are gangs in whom it appears that the cultural and economic conditions peculiar to that area are important factors contributing to the delinquency. However, not to minimize the importance of these social factors, one might wonder whether parent-child relationships are not also a cause in such gang delinquency. It is known that in such areas there are many families whose children do not succumb to the destructive temptations of their environment. In fact, many such children become fine citizens and occasionally outstanding leaders in our country. It is not the purpose of the authors in this book to become involved in a discussion of cultural and economic problems in which mere interest and passing knowledge do not indicate competence in evaluating these particular factors. Rather, in this chapter they will discuss the medical aspects of child delinquency.

In contrast with the gang delinquent, study of individual child delinquents and their parents in the physician's office by collaborative technic has revealed that in every instance the problem can be traced back to faulty emotional adjustments of parent and child. Although popularly blamed, the influence of comics, movies, bad companions and school teachers is minimal. The healthy child and parents, who do not have to stop to analyze their actions and feelings but are secure in their mutual honesty and love, are not influenced by such extraneous factors. The disturbed child and the disturbed parent find it easier to place the blame on such factors than to recognize their own contributions to the particular delinquency.

Delinquency results from a defect in one's conscience. The child derives his ideas of right and wrong from his parents' consciences. This is learned and not inherited. The mother and the father who really mean business when they tell the child what he should and should not do have no problems in making their wishes understood and obeyed. The child senses—and finds quickly—any loopholes that may be present in the parent's commands. The parent may say one thing but, by a half-smile, a tone of voice or a facial expression, may suggest something else.

For example, Mrs. Brown was knitting while reclining comfortably on a chair at the beach. Beyond the shade of her large umbrella, 4-year-old Tommy was poking teasingly at a large, strange police dog. "Tommy, honey, leave the man's dog alone." She yawned and resumed her knitting.

Twelve-year-old George went up to his father one bright Sunday morning and said petulantly, "Dad, Mother won't let me go to the swimming hole with the scouts. She says it's dangerous. The other boys can do a lot of things I'm not allowed to do. Sometimes, she's unfair." Father hesitated, raised his eyebrows, winced, drew a few puffs on his pipe, shrugged his shoulders, "Do what your mother says." There was no conviction in his voice. George knew he had a secret ally. He could go to the swimming hole.

Verbal prohibitions by the parent lose their meaning when the parent shows unusual interest in a given situation. Ten-year-old Mike obviously enjoyed telling his father in full detail, how he threw a rotten tomato at "that crabby old janitor" and then enjoyed the thrill of being chased and hunted—unsuccessfully—by the angry and tomato-splattered janitor. Mike's father, with a broad grin on his face, and nodding appreciatively, ate up every detail. His pride in Mike was obvious. When Mike finally completed his description with a loud, comradely laugh, his father felt he had to make some perfunctory statement in defense of propriety, "You know you should never do that again, Mike." And, with his arm over his son's shoulder, both went out together chuckling.

One of the most difficult loopholes with which the child must contend is double-talk by the parents. A child's feelings are very plastic and easily molded; he quickly senses and reacts to the hidden desires of his parents. This is even more easily accomplished by the child when the parent is two-faced or speaks out of both sides of his mouth at the same time. Although the parent tells the child what he cannot do, in the same breath he offers the child an alternative, a loophole to the prohibition.

Mrs. G. was horrified and glared at Linda when she said, "Linda, Miss Jones, your teacher, phoned me today and told me something I never would have believed. Mommy was very hurt. To think that my own little girl would be caught taking pennies from Miss Jones's purse. I'm so ashamed of you, Linda. Why did you ever have to do a thing like that? You have everything you want. Why couldn't you have taken pennies from Mommy's pocketbook? I always keep it by the toaster! Linda, what shall I do with you?" Linda's mother has an elastic conscience; it is not right to steal from the teacher, but it is right to take pennies from Mother's pocketbook without telling mother.

Another common way that a parent grants permission for what is verbally prohibited is by the parent's own double standards of conduct. The parent himself does what he forbids the child to do.

Mrs. D. insists that June always tell the truth and stay within her weekly allowance. "After all, Daddy is not made of money!" June bit her lip and looked wistfully at the new checkered skirt that her mother bought only yesterday on the installment plan while she and June were at the department store. June's thoughts drifted back to yesterday when her mother said, "Let's not tell Daddy now, June. He'd only get mad and worry about the money. And you know what the doctor said about his blood pressure!" Mr. V. sternly tells Jackie not to smoke, because smoking would stunt his growth. But, Jackie remembers Dad's repeated boast that he himself has been smoking since he was 12 years old and had his first cigarette behind the barn without his father's knowledge. Jackie's father is 6 feet tall and "strong as a horse."

There is no difference between a big lie or a little lie to the impressionable child. Parental lying shows the child that one may say one thing and mean another; that one may say one thing and then deny it; that one may promise one thing and do another. In this way, the lines of honesty can be drawn very carelessly. Lies in one situation spread to lies in many situations. Lying can show the child how to give lip service to a command or a promise without obeying or even without having any intention of obeying. It makes a sham out of law, morals, common decency and respect. The parent who is so concerned about his or her child's telling "fibs" would do better with some honest soul-searching of himself. What the child learns is learned from his parents.

Conscience is the deep, ineradicable memory of standards of conduct learned from the parents; it is a system of values of what is right and wrong, good and evil. It contains the seeds for the most lofty of human thoughts, feelings, and acts— and the most base. It determines how the individual will act. The learned code of ethics becomes a road map that tells a child what to do in meeting new situations throughout life. As in the construction of a skyscraper, one builds from the foundation up and does not start with the 50th story suspended in air. The development of conscience is an ever-present growth which starts at the beginning and goes on throughout life. It is not something that the parent can temporize with, by saying, "We can put this off until next time. He's too young anyway. Let's wait until he is older, and he'll understand." It is always a question of here and now, not some place else or some other time. Conscience is not static. It is continually resisting new pressures, changing conditions, and temptations, and it is continually being reinforced or altered by the impact of new experiences upon the previous ones. Therefore, the parent who is not

consistent in his own thoughts, feelings and actions will expose
the child to his own highly flexible and inconsistent set of rules.
The child's developing conscience will be like that of the parent; it will have all his defects, deficiencies and inconsistencies.
And, if the parent finds that his child's conscience is defective,
he should search his own conscience structure.

It is seen, then, that a conscience, built upon consistent
parental actions and principles, becomes not a list of specific
(and changing) rules for specific (and changing) situations but
a set of consistent principles applicable to virtually all situations.

Although the church, the school, the home and each new life
situation contribute to the reinforcement or alteration of the
conscience, the foundation is laid in the preschool years by the
parents. In this period the child is first learning the concept of
time, of what tomorrow means. The child begins to think of
growing up and wonders if he or she will be like the father and
the mother. Beyond this faint inkling of what the future means,
the concept of time is too difficult for the child to grasp. He
lives mainly from day to day; he understands only what he can
see, feel and hear today. He understands, further, only what is
happening to people that he knows in the place where he is. He
is literal. He is totally unequipped to understand ideas or
thought concepts which are presented to him as mere words.
Therefore, it is that which the easily pliable and highly recep-
tive young child experiences and knows to be true for himself
that molds him. What is merely told to him without accompanying feelings and actions is not important. The important thing is the substance, the constant interaction of feeling
between child and parent, not the form and the ritual. The
child learns by actual participation and by observation of actions and feelings. He does not learn from simply being told the
correct thing to do, when he observes otherwise.

"Tommy, how many times have I told you not to lie to me?"
But Tommy has just heard his mother tell Mrs. Williams on the
phone that she has a splitting headache and was so sorry she
could not play bridge that afternoon. Tommy knows better:
mother wants to spend the afternoon waxing the floors.

Similarly, what is read to the child or what the child reads is
of no importance if the child observes differently. As a matter

of fact, the child may actually see the parents observe, on a superficial basis, the accepted code of ethics, but knows that their deep feelings are different. Sensing these undercurrents, the child will make them his own, although he may actually see his parents go through the motions of acting otherwise. Thus, Mrs. F. is the leader in church and civic organizations. She can always be counted upon as a willing and helpful volunteer for any worthy cause. She is always ready to offer neighborly help for any of the minor but nevertheless numerous problems that can arise in a household. Thirteen-year-old Nancy constantly hears words of praise for her mother, Mrs. F. People cannot understand how such a wonderful and talented woman can have a child like Nancy: unfriendly, sarcastic, cynical and mistrusted by her classmates. But Nancy is tired of listening to the constant praise of her mother. She knows that her mother is really a different type of woman than her neighbors think. But, what can she say? She cannot be disloyal to her mother. And if she did tell, the neighbors never would believe her; they would only call Nancy ungrateful and badly spoiled. More tragic, however, is the fact that even when the child knows that the parent is definitely in the wrong, often the child will not tell on the parent, but rather will take the blame on her (the child's) own shoulders. Nancy has heard her mother say at the supper table, "I don't know why I bother with all these clubs. None of those committee women know anything! They are so stupid!" You know, Henry (the husband), I don't think Mrs. M. and her husband are getting along together. I'll bet he's going around with that new secretary I've heard about. But, serves Mrs. M. right. She's always such a mess. Doesn't know a thing about cosmetics." "That Mrs. Taylor bragging about her son. To hear her talk, you'd think he's another Einstein. As if there can be any geniuses in that family. You know that her father ran off with another woman. It's supposed to be a big secret. And that son she brags about, that little 'Einstein,' he's just an ordinary thief. Oh, I suppose I shouldn't say that. The poor boy only stole a bicycle. All the children have bikes these days. What can you expect of a father and a mother like that? In a case like theirs, I couldn't blame our Nancy if she stole a bicycle too." Not only is Mrs. F. showing her daughter, Nancy, her true hostile feelings toward her neighbors in a two-faced manner, but she is also telling Nancy that, in a given situation, stealing would be permissible. As if stealing in any situation and for any reason can ever be tolerated!

Mr. F., Nancy's father, is the perfect gentleman: always impeccably attired and handsomely groomed; he always knows the right thing to say for every occasion; he is a connoisseur of fine music and good food; his winning smile captivates. The women all envy Mrs. F. for having a husband with such cavalier qualities. Again, Nancy's experience differs. When she goes shopping with her father, he is always in a hurry, grabs her hand and practically drags her after him. He berates the clerks if they are at all slow or if he must wait for another customer. He finds fault with everything. He frequently makes a scene with the clerk and insists on seeing the store manager. Following one such scene, the intimidated and confused clerk gave Mr. F. his change and ran to the safety of another customer. Mr. F. counted the change, chortled and grunted as he quickly led Nancy away, "Stupid fool, serves him right. He gave me a dollar too much change. The store is making too much profit anyway." Of course, Nancy is not convinced by her father's gallant manner. She knows that her father really enjoys making people squirm and is not the kind of gentleman her mother's friends think he is. Without any pretensions other than a flimsy excuse, Mr. F. gave Nancy another lesson in dishonesty in the incident described above.

Mr. and Mrs. F. can quote the code of ethics of society and the laws of religion. Nancy may be taught these same rules at home and at Sunday school. But Nancy knows that her parents pay only lip service to such rules. They do not really live up to them or believe in them. Nancy has been taught by her parents to be the perfect lady, knowing when to rise, when to smile, what to say, when to say it and all the finer manners of etiquette. Like her parents, she presents all the outer appearances of conforming to the accepted rules of conduct; when her self-interest or whims are at stake, such rules are automatically set aside with such skill that the infractions may not even be recognized by those about her. And Nancy herself does not even realize that she is doing wrong.

Conscience is not a matter of intelligence. From the many examples already given, it is apparent that many of these people with obvious defects in their conscience are highly intelligent. Other examples could be cited in which the intelligence was below average, and yet the conscience was sound. In these people, their consciences compensate in a measure for their below-average intelligence. They can hold down jobs that require loyalty, honesty and dependability.

A frequent and important problem that arises during this period of developing conscience is what the parent should do when the child steals for the first time. This is a very common problem, and almost every child has done it at least once in his life. If the parent handles the problem, when it first occurs, directly and honestly, the situation will not recur. What should be done? As Mrs. R. leaves the department store with Johnny, she notices for the first time that he is carrying a toy monkey. In a natural matter-of-fact voice, she asks Johnny where he got the toy. She does not accuse him nor does she show undue excitement or interest. Finding out that Johnny took it from a counter in the store, Mrs. R. said, "You know that the toy monkey does not belong to you. You should never take what is not yours." Since this is her son's first such act, Mrs. R. realizes that he does not really know the meaning of what he has done. It is her job now to show him that what he did is wrong and naughty. Without any fuss or lengthy explanations, she returns with Johnny to the toy counter, finds the clerk and explains, in Johnny's presence, just what happened. The clerk, used to this situation with young children, fully understands and takes the toy back. Johnny is told again that he has been very naughty and must never again take anything that does not belong to him. Then, to discourage any repetition of stealing, Mrs. R. withholds from Johnny some other toys or does not permit him to do something or get something that he enjoys. For example, Mrs. R. gave Johnny no desserts for one week and did not buy him any ice cream cones. Johnny's father fully supported his wife. He did not make any deals with Johnny that would undo the mother's punishment. He fully knew what happened and completely subscribed to the punishment.

The value of the stolen article is unimportant. Stealing any article, expensive or inexpensive, under any conditions, is always forbidden. Permitting the stealing of any article, no matter how trifling and inexpensive, gives tacit parental approval for further stealing.

If Johnny had been permitted to keep the toy monkey and nothing had been said or done except the admonition, "You are naughty; you should never do that again!" Johnny would have enjoyed the use of the toy. In such a situation, what his mother told him would have had no meaning compared with the fact that he kept and was enjoying the toy. Such acts would be repeated. Johnny would steal. As has been stated repeatedly in this book—and it cannot be stated too emphatically—it is the underlying feelings, not the acts and the words, which are of paramount importance in this and any situation. The parent may make an empty ritual of words and actions in strictly following the procedure used by Johnny's mother. However, if the accompanying feelings for honesty are not present in the household, the child never will learn honesty.

The parent may show undue excitement and consternation on first discovering that the child has stolen. The parent who is overcome by fear that the child may grow up to be a thief often shows undue excitement and flies into a tirade of abuse. "You thief; you dirty little thief. Steal! Steal! You rotten thief! How can you steal! How can you do such a dirty thing? I'll break you in two! I'll show you! Steal! Steal, will you? If I ever catch you doing this again . . . Steal! How could you do such a thing? How could you? You . . . You thief! If I ever catch you doing this again . . . !" Rather than effectively dealing with the stealing in a straight-forward way that the child will understand, this parent only communicates to the child his own overwhelming fear that this is the first of many acts of stealing. The child quickly senses the parent's fear that the stealing might get out of hand and that it will be repeated. An alternative to complete future honesty has been shown. The parent's intense excitement only indicates the parent's own underlying uncertainty over the concept of honesty. Why should the parent who is basically honest and sure of his own honesty fear that his child will develop otherwise? The child learns that there really are two possible roads that may be taken: one may steal or not steal. Johnny R., on the other hand, was given no alternative. There was only one road: he could not steal. However, in the instance of the parent with the emotional tirade a thought (and therefore implied permission) was implanted in the child that the stealing would get out of hand and be repeated.

In addition to the emotional tirade already discussed, there are other ways for the parent to communicate this distrust to the child. "Doctor, I was afraid that he'd break into somebody's house. I took the precaution of secretly following him so I'd be sure he was getting into no trouble." Such bizarre precautions only indicate how marked is the parent's deep distrust of his child. The child cannot help but sense this distrust even if he does not detect that his parent is secretly following him. The distrust is communicated from parent to child in many subtle ways. Without apparent reason, the parent quizzes the child: where has he been; with whom has he been; what has he done; how long was he there; is he sure; is he telling everything; is all the time accounted for; did he forget to mention something? The child knows that the parent is suspicious. With the passage of time and constant exposure to such a suspicious parent, the child himself gradually succumbs to this malignantly distrustful attitude which he in turn may apply to many of his own life-situations. Other subtle and treacherous ways include checking the contents of the child's pockets, smelling the handkerchief, secretly reading the child's notes or diary, questioning the child's friends on the child's activities and the parent's checking by phone or by actually making the trip himself to make sure that his child is actually where he said he would be. The parent often consoles himself with the thought that the child does not detect all these clandestine parental signs of distrust.

But, even were this true, there are other even more important ways of communicating parental feelings and deceit to the child. As the child tells the parent the activities of the previous night, the child comes to a part which might lead to something immoral or off-color. The parent leans forward with intense interest and apparent anticipation. Momentarily, there is an expression of disapproval at what might come. But nothing out of line is mentioned. The interest rapidly wanes. The knowing smile, the dirty look, the arched eyebrow, the clucking sound with tongue, the impatient tap of fingers and foot, the disdainful blowing of smoke rings from the cigarette, the nervous whistle, the muttering of half-heard oaths, the clearing of the throat, the self-conscious inspection of ceiling or floor, the repeated nose-blowing, the ribald laughter, the inappropriate guffaws and the "come-on" expressed in the tone of voice—all these in endless variations and combinations can show a parental reaction entirely inconsistent with what the parent says. The child learns from the parent how the parent really feels—and this is parental permission.

"But Doctor, I don't see why you keep asking me questions about myself. And why do you keep asking about my father? That was a long time ago and has nothing to do with this situation. My Robert is a firebug because of his heredity. And what can you do about that? My husband's Uncle Joe had to be sent away because of setting barns on fire. And many of Robert's friends have been no better. Robert is the only one of my 5 children who sets fires or does anything wrong, so the cause must be outside our home. Please, Doctor, just give me some pills for my nerves—this is very upsetting, and I don't want to discuss it anymore."

Firesetting, like lying, stealing and sexual difficulties, results from parental problems and defects in conscience concerning the specific delinquency. Bad heredity is frequently given by the parent as the reason or excuse for a delinquency: "And what can you do about heredity?" There is no scientific evidence to support this opinion. But in every case of child delinquency where the parents and the child have been thoroughly studied by the collaborative technic, the physicans can always find specific emotional factors at the bottom of each delinquency. Of course, in practically all instances the parents are unaware of their connection with the problems. Nor are they aware that they themselves have any problems. These problems are based on intangible feelings and values; they cannot be seen, touched or heard. Though present, they cannot be grasped. What cannot be seen concretely, touched or heard is often difficult to understand or believe. And often, in these cases, one does not want to understand or believe, because the cause lies within oneself and not in an outside situation or in another person. Therefore, there are repeated denials and the constant search for scapegoats: placing the blame on heredity, bad companions, the school and even acts of God. "It is not in our stars but in ourselves." But the parent whose own feelings are shaping his child's actions and feelings was in turn molded by the feelings of his parents. It is a repeated cycle. Generation follows generation. And the feelings of one generation subtly inoculate and influence the feelings and the actions of the next. These same mechanisms apply to mental health as well as to disease. Stated another way, the parent whose own disturbed feelings flowed from those of his parents before him may not be to blame (since he had no control over the process), but nevertheless he is fully responsible. If this destructive cycle is ever to be broken, a spade must be called a spade, and responsibility for the delinquency must be firmly established. Flimsy excuses, rationalizations, vacillations, knowing smiles, deceptive winks, loopholes and the like must be recognized for what they are. Unless the attitudes of the home and society in general are changed, each succeeding generation will be inoculated with the destructive and unhealthy feelings of the old. This vicious cycle can be interrupted only by a complete understanding of the way the parent, through his own defective conscience and emotional problems, uses his child as a destructive outlet. It is far better that the parent in question find the outlet for his own inner tensions through himself and have some disabling emotional or psychosomatic illness than to have his defects in conscience and emotional problems find outlet by appearing in his child. Naturally, it is easier on the parent to have his child, rather than himself, disabled by these defects and problems. This poses no problem to the parent, because he often does not even know of the existence of the defect or the problem or that he is even passing these on to the child. It is far simpler to take the easy way out and thus appear to be the innocent victim of tragic circumstances

before an indulgent and misinformed society. The child takes
the rap from society for his parents. The newspaper headlines
and radio accounts unwittingly enforce and condone, with
sensational headlines, the parent's defective conscience:
"Mother in Tears As Son Is Sentenced for Shooting Playmate."

"If it is an emotional problem in the parents, Doctor, I can't
see why all my children are not affected equally. Of my 5
children, only Tony steals." The same question may be
phrased differently to ask why the older child, the middle
child, the boy, the girl, or the adopted child has the delinquency while the rest of the children do not. From what has
already been stated in this chapter, the specific delinquency in
the child represents specific emotional problems in the parent
which are not recognized as such by the parent. However,
these emotional problems cause a continual buildup of emotional tension in the parent for which he finds a suitable outlet through a specific child. This affords the parent vicarious
gratification, because the child does that which he, the parent,
would like to do because of his own emotional needs but
which he, the parent, dares not do because of his fear of the
opprobrium of society. Again, it must be repeated that the
parent is unaware that he even has a problem, let alone that
there is a connection between his specific problem and the
child's specific delinquency. The parent who vicariously finds
an outlet for his pent-up emotional needs and tension, through
one or possibly more children, has no need to involve the rest
of the children. The parent has found a satisfactory means of
relieving his inner tension; there is no need to look for other
outlets.

The selection of the scapegoat child conforms to these seemingly same irrational, illogical and definitely emotional processes of which the parent is totally unaware. However,
the physician who has fully and adequately studied both parent and child finds many definite and specific reasons why the
particular child has been made the scapegoat. This child may
be the only daughter in a family whose mother's emotional
problem was with her own mother. The delinquent girl's
mother may have had a relatively healthy relationship with

her own father, and therefore the sons escaped. The position of the child in the family, the name, the physical appearance (color of hair, shape of nose, voice) or the sex might determine which child will be the scapegoat.

For example, Andy, the firebug, was the oldest boy and looked like his Uncle Joe, the black sheep of the family who was sent away for setting barns on fire. Andy's father, who was the youngest of two sons, always played second fiddle to his brother, Joe. Joe got everything despite the fact that he always was in trouble. Andy's father was always blamed for Joe's many misdeeds. Joe was always praised; his parents never said a kind word when Andy's father did well in school. Andy's father always tried to prove to his parents and himself that he was better than Joe. Despite excellent grades in school, good deportment, and running a newspaper route to earn his own spending money, his parents took all this for granted. They lavished all their fond hopes and attentions on Joe. Joe's brother, Andy's father, resented such favoritism, but was forced to maintain silence; he had to contain his anger within himself until he finally found relief through his son's delinquency.

Young Georgie, who was in reform school for stealing was named after his mother's brother. Uncle George was the skeleton in the family closet and always was involved in truancy in school, accidents, petty stealing and later in molesting girls. When younger, Uncle George took delight in tormenting his sister, young Georgie's mother. Uncle George had been his own mother's pet. As a young girl, young Georgie's mother always had resented the favoritism shown to her brother. She never could fight back. Her brother was always right; she was always wrong. Even when the brother's taunts were cruelly excessive, the parents merely stood by and smiled or told her to stop upsetting George. Her parents never offered any help. These early experiences became indelible memories of bitter resentment. Through young Georgie, his mother found an outlet for the resentment that she had been forced to contain until that time. Young Georgie's two older sisters had no problems. His mother found complete relief for her warped emotions through her son; she needed no other outlet. Young

Georgie, like his uncle before him, was destined to become another family "skeleton in the closet."

Therefore, the problem of childhood delinquency is not only the matter of punishing the youthful offender but, more important, searching for the cause and establishing responsibility at the source. The individual case of delinquency represents a highly destructive unwitting partnership between the parent and the child.

CHAPTER 14

Sexual Problems

Another problem which frequently presents itself in the physician's office is that of sexual disturbances in children. The complaints are often disguised, minimized or distorted. The child's parent may bring the patient to the physician ostensibly for some triviality but in reality for the sexual disturbance which upsets parent and child. When the physician shows a sympathetic interest and does not sit in judgment by word, expression or tone of voice, the parents almost invariably discuss the child's problems.

With the complete collaborative study of the child and both parents as done with the other forms of delinquency, there is revealed, in sexual problems in children, the same direct causative relationships between the child's problems and those of one or both parents. As in other areas of human emotion, the parents may not and usually do not recognize even the existence of their own sexual problems. Or, if they do recognize the existence of such problems, they fully believe that they will not affect the children, because, "we never talk about these things in front of the children." As shown in previous chapters, when an emotional problem exists, tension constantly builds up. An outlet is needed. The built-up tension boils over. The release of this tension affects both parent and child in many emotional and physical areas, but when such tension is due to parental sexual problems, it spills over to the sexual feelings and attitudes of the child. This relationship is, if anything, easier for the physician to discover in sexual than in the other forms of delinquency.

When the problems of asthma and bed-wetting were discussed, it became apparent that frequently the parents of such children were sexually maladjusted with each other. The excessive hugging of the father and the daughter, and of mother and son and the sleeping, bathing and dressing practices described in those previous chapters were, it was shown, not truly an expression of parental love or modern frankness. Such practices, with hidden feelings of parental hate at the core, only serve to keep the child very young at a safer and less emotionally charged level of development, the mouth and the bowel stages; he cannot progress through the barriers of the first romance stage. Furthermore, as a partial price for this "modern frankness," such a child often develops, in addition to possible asthma and bed-wetting, much confusion over his or her role as a boy or a girl. The boy may become extremely passive (a feminine attribute), and the girl extremely aggressive (a male attribute). These changes serve to destroy the boy's basic role as a male and the girl's role as a female. In those examples, the mother, who had basic underlying conflicts with men from her own past, had unwittingly revenged herself on a man; the father, with similar problems with women, had unwittingly revenged himself on a woman. What had been called parental love and modern frankness had in fact served only to harm and destroy. There are, of course, innumerable other ways in which the many varieties of parental sexual maladjustments are reflected in the child.

At this point it should be said that sexuality in the child is different from that in the adult. It means how comfortable the child feels in the presence of his own sex as well as the opposite sex. It also means how successfully he has fulfilled his own role as a boy or a girl. Does the boy play football and basketball, climb trees and in general act like a Tom Sawyer or a Huckleberry Finn? Does the girl play with dolls, have tea parties and help mother around the house? Does the boy act like a boy, and the girl like a girl? The difference between the two sexes, therefore, is not only the anatomic difference but also—and surely as important—the differences in attitudes, feelings and values attached to their own and the opposite sex (see p. 38).

Very early in life, as has already been shown in this book, the child knows the anatomic differences between boys and

girls and men and women. It should be recalled that it was
during the first romance stage that the boy and the girl first
noticed the physical differences in their bodies. They showed
their healthy curiosity by their reactions and their many questions. It was at this time that the child really learned by
example from his parents as well as by the behavior of other
grown-ups that little boys and little girls and men and women
act and are treated differently. This is learned—and learned
chiefly from the parents. Its importance cannot be over-
stated, because, barring some rare trick of nature, the little
boy and the little girl undoubtedly will develop into a man
and a woman with all the adult physical attributes of their
sex. How well the adult man and woman adjust to, work
with and enjoy life with members of their own and opposite
sex depends on their values and feelings in this regard learned
from their parents. It is also most often these same feelings
and seldom any recognized physical disease that account for
how well grown-ups function sexually as men and women.
The frigid woman and the impotent man with rare exceptions
are anatomically normal but physically disabled because of
emotional problems stemming from their early childhood.
Unfortunately, as has been shown repeatedly, this problem
will continue from generation to generation. Innocent children are robbed of their future as happy and healthy men and
women by flagrant and highly destructive household nudity
and lurid sleeping and bathing practices which extend all too
often into the child's pubertal or even postpubertal years.
Modern frankness is nothing less than a complete perversion of
the traditional role of parent toward child. The parent is
supposed to help and teach his child, not to hurt and betray.
The parent is not supposed to use his or her own child as an
outlet for his own unresolved problems, tensions and conscience defects. Although the parent may not be to blame for
these terrible problems (which stem from his or her own
childhood), the parent is certainly responsible to see to it
that he does not perpetuate this corruption.

The problems of the parent reveal themselves in the child
not only after he has grown up but also while he is still a
growing youngster. In general, society treats these problems,

in child and adult, with a close-mouthed, hush-hush attitude. A frank approach to a few illustrative problems will show this definite and tragic relationship between parent and child.

January 3. This afternoon 19-year-old Pete's mother came in for an interview. She is 49 years old, a huge, aggressive woman who was dressed in very gayly colored clothes and wore a large felt hat with decorative flowers. She looked at least 10 years younger than her stated age. She immediately took a chair in close proximity to the physician's desk and started to talk in a highly modulated, histrionic voice. She said that one of Peter's bad habits was telling wild stories. "It's a failing. His brother and sister suffer from these stories. For instance, when Johnny had his operation for a tight heart valve, Peter wrote his pals to say that his own finger was being amputated. Also doctor, tell me, did he have transfusions when his teeth were extracted the other day? That's what he told me just a little while ago. When applying for a job, he built himself up to say that he was a great athlete, that he had made many records. However, the only thing he was ever great at was being a rifleman."

[Peter told many lies. It will be interesting to see why he does so.]

"He is a very nervous and high-strung fellow. I think the trouble is really due to a fall he had from a bicycle at the age of 6. He was out at the City Hospital then."

[All sorts of diseases and injuries, and especially head injuries, are frequently blamed, without medical justification, by the parents and patients for all sorts of behavior problems. This is another common scapegoat mechanism (see p. 127).]

The mother then related some of the background factors surrounding Peter's current hospitalization. She stated that Peter was a poor student in school and that he always played with boys much younger than himself. He would bring them home from school and take them hunting and ice-skating. She said she never suspected anything was wrong and never knew anything until her husband got a phone call from the police out of state. Soon thereafter, Peter returned and explained his trouble with the law by saying, "I blacked out." Peter's

mother said that while thinking his problem over, she remembered that when he was 8 years of age, she had a fear that
he would molest little girls by pulling their dresses up.

[A child begins life with a clean slate: no fears or abnormal
thoughts. Here however, is a mother who has a very unusual
fear concerning her son. Peter cannot help but be aware of
this fear. Is she not putting ideas into his mind?]

Some of the very potentially dangerous homicidal elements
are well illustrated by the following quotations. "We were
called by the police who said Peter was keeping boys out in a
cabin, that he wanted them to join a club. He claims he's
never harmed them. He gave the boys an enema. He says
he's afraid he's going to hurt somebody, or injure them, to
strike them. He's a great one to handle guns. I though he'd
shoot someone if the little kids resisted him. I don't understand, because one of the boys said his father was a
policeman."

[The significance of the enema will become clear as this
case history unfolds. Note the mother's fear of Peter's doing
violence.]

When Peter's mother was asked how she imagined her son
became this way, she said that he was a lone wolf as a child
and that the only time he ever had taken a girl out was when
she, Peter's mother, had insisted that he do so for the Junior
Prom. "He always has been afraid of girls." When he was
13, a neighbor woman said, "Have you ever suspected little
Peter of molesting girls? He threatened to give them all an
enema." "However," continued Peter's mother, "I questioned
the girls and asked them if he picked up their dresses or
touched them. They said, 'No,' so I wasn't worried.

"Concerning sex, Doctor, Peter and I talked these things
over, that is about girls and where babies came from when he
was 12 or 13. Yet he seemed to know it all. When he was
in the bathroom I frequently would go in, and he wouldn't
mind. You see, Peter was never circumcised, and it bothered
me. His foreskin was too tight. I always checked it until he
was 7. I'd tell him to clean it out good. He was always pulling
at himself. We changed doctors and the doctor said, 'No, it
wouldn't do any harm.' I thought it was very bad for him to

do this. When he was older, I was afraid he wouldn't take care of his foreskin. I thought that this might cause the testicles to shrink."

[In no uncertain terms the mother is communicating her own preoccupation with her son's genitals to him in a very frightening manner. She conveys to him her fear that harm may be done.]

"When he was older, he had a room to himself, but even to this day, if I'm stretched out [nude] taking a nap, he'd enter my room and I wouldn't be ashamed of my body." Peter's mother then volunteered the information that dressing was very open in her house; that she frequently walked around with only her brassière and panties on; and that it didn't make any difference to the children.

[At this point, the reader should be very leery of the complete lack of modesty in this household. Let Peter's mother continue with these verbatim quotations in their original sequence.]

"He always had rectal troubles, and I gave him enemas, but today I no longer worry, since I feed him plenty of vegetables and fruits which make him regular. So, when home, he'd say he didn't have any troubles. At 10 years of age I gave him many enemas for nervousness. Lately, he's been affectionate again. He kisses me when leaving and coming. When young, he never liked thunder and lightning. He'd come and sleep with us. Quite recently we went to a hotel and we shared the same bed and room, Peter and I. It made no difference."

[Again, one may note the mother's fixation on rectal troubles and enemas. A 19-year-old boy sharing the same bed with his mother!]

Peter's mother said that although she explained menstruation to him, he had "never seen that. He was an instrument baby and weighed over 9 pounds at birth. I cried when the doctor told me it was a boy; I had set my heart on having a little girl." She then described her pregnancy and how sick she was, vomiting throughout the pregnancy and how "hard put" she was in the early feeding: "breast fed him, weighed him, breast fed him again, and he'd always cry." The mother mentioned with some interest, how "abnormally shaped and pointed Peter's head was at birth."

[In her wandering disconnected talk, it is evident that Peter's troubles were determined long before the first romance stage, even before he was born. Peter's mother was preoccupied with her son's alleged abnormalities from the first day of life. Her only memories of his infancy were unpleasant ones.]

"As Peter became older, he always preferred to visit with older people, because of his trouble in getting along with children his own age. I kept changing schools. I was very concerned about his sexual development. I kept waiting for him to start having wet dreams. I would carefully look over and smell the bed sheets to be sure. Yet, he only had it once! At that time, I noticed tissue in the waste paper basket, and he said that he had a headache."

[Note the maternal preoccupation with sex.]

January 7. Today Peter entered the office, and the physician put him into a deep hypnotic trance. He returned to periods in his earlier childhood and relived many upsetting situations that occurred at that time and had since been forgotten. Hypnosis permitted him to remember, relive and describe many experiences which he otherwise may not have remembered. However, the physician suspected experiences such as these from information that Peter's mother supplied as well as from Peter's dreams. Before going into the trance he had very little to say about his progress and nothing to say about his family. While in the trance the following incidents were relived.

1. "Dad's holding me in his arms. I kick my mother. She's going to give me an enema. There's a pillow on the floor. My dad is laying me down on my side. Getting a bad tummy ache out of it. I have a bottle [presumably to suck on]. She's looking at me very angrily. She wants me to go on some more. I'm lying on the bed." During this period the patient jumped, kicked and winced.

2. "I see myself buying an erector set in a store. I have to buy one. I take it home and play with it. Mother comes down

and sees me, she asks me where I got it. She says Dad will have to find out about it. She makes me sit in a corner by myself. I make up a story when Dad comes in. I try to get out of it. I'm scared that I'll get a spanking. I try to run away. Dad catches me and tells me to take my clothes off. Mother is standing in the kitchen. I ask her to help, but she says nothing. Dad calls and gets a big stick. Sister and brother will hear everything. He's spanking me. I break away. He catches me behind the table. He's beating me. It hurts awful." At this point Peter is crying and jerking all over. "My brother is coming upstairs with a hamburger and a cake. He must feel sorry for me.

3. "I go to the park where young boys are. I play I'm a doctor at the hopsital. I tell them I want to give a physical examination. We go up by the lake. I have one watching from the tree and one watching on the road. I get the other one undressed. I feel nervous and tense. I take his pulse, examine his chest and sexual organs. I check his back and rectum. Put a stick up his rectum, and he doesn't object. I check under his knees and between his toes. He says he will join my club. I initiate him with 5 whacks on his feet. I beat him until he cries, and he says he won't tell. I feel pins and needles all over me." At this point the patient repeatedly pulls his legs rapidly apart and together again and jerks all over.

[Peter shows the same preoccupation with the rectum and the genital organs that his mother has shown all his life. Peter does to the little boy the same thing that was done to him when his mother gave him the repeated enemas. Peter's confusion between the organs of sex and elimination is apparent as is his underlying hatred. Peter whips as he has been whipped.]

4. "I see Gloria; she's not old. I see her downstairs. I tell her I'll examine her. She says, 'Yes.' I undress her, look at her. I try to do the same thing Mommy and Daddy do. Gloria yells. I pull it out. It's like giving her an enema so she'll feel better. But I put it in front instead of the rectum. She doesn't mind."

[It would seem that Peter had learned his precocity by observing his parents in their laxity with their open-door policy.

Even more important than actual observation is the previously discussed unbridled maternal interest in sex. Again the same preoccupations and confusions between adult sexual practices and enemas appear.]

5. "I know I'm going to be caught, but I keep on doing these things. I can't stop myself. I have to keep on going. I'm driving to Junction City. Feel somebody is watching me. Two cops pull up in a car. First they ask me if I'm crazy. My mind is going blank. They put me in jail, and I told the others [prisoners] I stole a Cadillac. I don't want them to know what I really did."

[Although Peter knows that what he does is wrong, and although he is ashamed of his abnormal actions, he cannot help himself. He must go on even with the certainty that he will eventually be caught and punished by the law. Peter is driven on by a devil which he cannot resist. But this devil is not a mysterious force out of mythology or scientific gobble-dygook: it is a very sick, badly confused individual of flesh and blood—his mother. Unless this problem is recognized and uprooted at its source before it can permanently cripple the growing child, the child and society must suffer. The growing child becomes the young man who is already lost by the time he first comes to the attention of the law. Peter and his mother should have seen a physician many years previously. In fact, Peter's mother should have seen a physician when she herself was young, long before her marriage.]

6. "The doctor is in my room giving me a shot with a big needle. Mother pulls my pajamas off. She has me by my sex organs. It hurts. She rolls me over. The needle hurts. She takes a nice long look all over me.

7. "I'm nude in the bathroom. Mother comes in with a yard-stick, spanks me for filling my pants. I hate her! I could kill her! I'm going to kill her! She has given me many spankings like this. I'm mad! She has done this before! I'm mad! I'm going to kill her when I get out of here!"

[The unnaturally close relationship between Peter and his mother and her hatred for him have had their effect. This mother's life is really in danger. It is often feelings such as these that lead children to kill their parents.]

8. "I'm out trying sexual intercourse with a neighbor girl. She says yes. We get off her bike and we go into the woods. Feels good. She says that we should go back.

9. "I'm with Aunt Louise, father's sister, on a trip. We're in a motel; it's bedtime. I forgot my pajamas. She says it's OK. I sleep in my shorts and she undresses down to her bloomers and brassière. Crawl into bed together. I'm scared. I'm only 12. I'm afraid to go to sleep. I'm awake all night."

[More evidences of wholesale "modern frankness." This time it is from the father's side of the family.]

January 16

10. "I see myself and 4 others in jail. I'm supposed to have molested some boys in the tennis club. They tell me I'm going on trial. Now I'm going up to the courthouse to see the judge for the hearing. I plead innocent. They said a young boy told them I gave him a spanking and checked his pulse. I started crying, because I don't remember it, and I'm scared. The judge tells me to go home and get out of town by sun-down, otherwise I'll be prosecuted. I'm brought to the railroad station. I'm scared. I didn't do it. I'm getting off the train now and meeting my dad. He's getting me to tell what happened. He's quite mad. I feel I've been gypped."

When pressed by the physician and told that he really could remember and that there must be complete honesty, Peter said the following:

"Dad wanted me to tell him. I have a young boy in the basement of the tennis club. I'm giving him an enema. The manager catches me and calls the police. I've been caught red-handed. It's true! It's true all the way! It's true! I tell Dad I can't remember, 'cause I'm afraid to tell him. He keeps trying. He gives up. He thinks it's all a big story. I never told the truth too much. Mother knows, yet she doesn't say a word. Keeps me in suspense all the time. I'm worried about it. I wish she'd let me know. She just gives me a mean look all the time. I wonder if Mother will beat me for misbehaving at the tennis club. I'm scared of Mother. I don't like her anymore. She never did me any good. She babied me and made me feel too young. She always sends me to the doctor, because my foreskin is too tight. The doctor said it's all right. I feel I'm not sexually all there. She says I have to pull it back. She pulls it back. Looks well pleased. It's mine and I should do what I want with it! She doesn't mind too much if I play with smaller boys. She doesn't encourage me to go with girls. I feel it from the way she acts. She doesn't want me to go with older boys. I want to run away from home. She examines my testicles. I have no will power to stop her, and I think she's doing right. My mother would say I'm lying if I ever told my Dad about this."

[Peter is terrified about what the law will do to him, but he cannot help himself. He is even more terrified of his parents on whom he has learned not to depend. Worse still, he realizes that his mother knows, but she says nothing. Her silence gives tacit permission for continued similar misdeeds. After all, Peter has long been aware of his mother's overwhelming interest in sex. The mother much prefers that Peter not go out with girls or older boys but only with younger boys. Again the mother is the motivating force. The mother is supposed to help the child, but in this case she is encouraging his interest in unnatural, highly destructive acts. And, worse still, Peter has no one he can trust. He knows that if he were to tell his father what his mother is doing, she would lie and deny. He stands alone, frightened and totally unable to stop his steady march to destruction. His mother repeatedly brings Peter to physicians not for the many obvious and serious emotional problems but only to use the medical profession as a tool of her own perversity.]

11. "I want to go to work or join the service. She's to blame for my troubles, for getting me here. I wanted revenge on young boys, the age she used to work on me all the time. She wants me to become a doctor. She always did."

Peter then told how his mother made a special point of stepping out of the shower on some faint pretext to talk to him and that he was very frightened when she so exposed herself to him.

"I'm afraid to go with other girls, because they'll do the same thing, undress in front of me. It makes me scared and uneasy."

January 20. Today Peter's father came to the office. He is a middle-aged, tall, well-built, business man who is most passive in his demeanor. He had to be beckoned into the room three times before he entered. He has the appearance of prosperity in his sporty clothes and in his frequent allusion to business trips to California and Hawaii. He very quickly started to discuss what he thinks are the causative factors in Peter's illness. "Peter was the first child, an instrument baby. Perhaps his fall from the bicycle 15 years ago was responsible. Ever since that time he has had a terrific imagination." The father then expanded further on Peter's management of his finances in which he had "many bad streaks." However, the father's conscience defect about money is evident in the way he counseled Peter. Peter was in trouble with several loan sharks and installment-buying agencies. The father always bailed him out of financial trouble with fresh transfusions of money and even bought him flashy sport cars.

[By continually bailing his son out of his financial difficulties, the father only encouraged further difficulties.]

The father continued, "I nagged him all the time about whether his fingernails were clean or not." Following one of the most recent court incidents, the father said that he reminded his son, "Now, Peter, if you feel that coming on, your weakness, let me know, so I can help you."

[With all of Peter's serious problems, this father worries about his son's keeping his fingernails clean! He does not forcefully tell Peter, "No, you must not and cannot do it." Instead there is the bland, ". . . Let me know so I can help you." By not forcefully setting definite limits, the father is, in effect, giving, as he had done in the past, permission for other similar acts.]

The father frequently spoke about Peter as though he were a 5-year-old rather than a boy in his 'teens. He described Peter's illness as, "It's a cross of life we have to bear." The father's own attitudes toward Peter's difficulties were well summarized by his parting remarks. "I was always scared he'd attack a child. I told him as long as I can remember, way before this, 'Always remember your actions, Peter. You know the stuff you read in the papers. I'm worried. I'd hate to see my own children attacked.' Gee, Doc., my own son looks like a criminal!"

Despite all the foregoing evidence to the contrary, the father looks upon Peter's problems as an act of God. Like the mother, Peter's father fears his son will be delinquent. Not only that, but he also communicated these fears to Peter verbally and directly. Why should a parent, secure in his own conscience structure, fear that the child will be anything but completely normal and law-abiding? The father thinks that his son looks like a criminal! Fond parents may see in their children evidences of the future musician, physician, contractor, accountant and so on, but to see evidences of criminality. . . . ! !

The same general principles described in Peter's case apply to the girl who indulges in abnormal sexual play with girls as Peter did with boys. Such a girl becomes the woman who never makes a satisfactory emotional and sexual adjustment with men and prefers women. Rather than love which they claim is the motivating force in their choice of behavior, hatred is really the determining factor. Although not mentioned as frequently in talk and print, this preference of woman for woman is as common as the preference of man for man. In the case of the man, society actively abhors the situation; in the case of the woman, society frequently, tolerantly closes its eyes.

CHAPTER 15

The Boy Who Thinks He Is a Girl

Transvestitism

Man or woman? Boy or girl? There are boys who are so confused about their own sexuality that they may go so far as to dress like girls. Boys who are passive and have many feminine qualities and girls who are aggressive and have many masculine qualities have been mentioned many times in previous examples.

Placed further along the scale of this character disturbance are boys who are boys in an anatomic sense only. They feel like girls; they act like girls; they even dress like girls. They wish they were actually girls. When they grow up, some even undergo mutilating surgery in an attempt to change their genitals to fool themselves as well as the world at large. In spite of parental misinformation and superstitions to the contrary, these individuals are boys. Remove their clothes, examine them and do laboratory tests to check their actual hormone levels in the body, and one will find them to be boys. Transvestites are completely different from those exceedingly rare cases of disturbed physical and hormone structure in which the two sexes are truly mixed in the same body. In transvestites, the confusion concerning sex is in the emotions and not in the body structure, hormones and fluids. How does this confusion occur?

Fifteen-year-old Pat is talking to the physician. "Mother and Daddy called me Tillie until I was 6 years old . . . and they did not cut my hair until then. Mother really wanted a girl. Then I came.. I had yellow curly hair and big blue eyes. She always dressed me in girl's clothes until I was 6 years old and had to go to school. But even after that, Mother would try my sister's clothes on me. If I looked very nice, she'd tell me. One day I tried Mother's high-heeled shoes, black silk dress, lipstick and fingernail polish. I was 8 years old then. Mother came in and laughed, 'Tillie, what would your father say? I don't know why you must do things like this. Don't let me ever catch you outside dressed like this. What would our neighbors think?' She then looked at me, smiled, 'Oh! come on Patty; I can't get mad at you!' She hugged me and kissed me."

[Note that the mother never simply and firmly said, "No!" Her way of saying "no" had many loopholes. "Don't ever let me catch you outside dressed like this." Does that mean that such actions are all right in other circumstances such as inside the home? She is more alarmed over what the neighbors will think than what her child is doing. And then, certainly her closing remarks and embraces gave further permission for the repetition of such acts.]

"Another time, Mother told me what a trial it was [pregnancy and delivery] . . . she told me she had her heart set on a girl . . . I wish for Mother's sake that I were a girl to help her . . . if I were a little girl I could stay home and help . . . I used to wait many hours [at night] for her to sneak in [my room], tuck me in and kiss me good night. I was the only one she was close enough to, to sleep with . . . I like to bake, cook, make pies and cakes and clean the kitchen . . . she always said I shouldn't abuse myself [masturbate], because I would become dull and lifeless. She showed me neighborhood children [who did it] . . . Mother was always open, and she bathed with me until last year, because she loved me and wanted to be close to me. Only a few times did she have disagreements with father . . . he was oversexed. She told me he was too demanding . . . regardless of her physical tiredness, he forced his attentions on her."

[This mother not only slept and bathed with her son beyond pubertal years (unfortunately not a rare occurrence), but she also discussed with her son the secrets of her own physical relationship with her husband. It is apparent that Pat's mother has done everything to achieve her desire to have a little girl. Unfortunately, nature gave her a little boy which she unwittingly transformed into a little girl in feelings, clothes and actions. In doing so, she has ruined her son's future as a man. By her actions it can be seen that she not only permitted but fostered this transformation.]

"Father is a farmer and works very hard all the time. Once he threw me into the creek . . . it was over my head. I was quite scared . . . we never understood each other. I felt I wasn't good enough . . . he was unfair and not understanding. Couldn't agree with him . . . when little, he'd beat me all the time.

"My oldest sister was closest to me. We went on trips overnight together. She tried to do the things I liked. We used to fix [castrate] the baby pigs. It would get me very nervous, because it was painful and cruel."

[Here is a boy who remained close to his mother and imitated her rather than the father he feared. A farmer's son is used to seeing pigs castrated, and, under usual circumstances, accepts this as another common aspect of farm life. It would seem plausible that Pat's overreaction to such castration might be related to the extreme mutilation he has endured in every aspect of his sexuality except the physical.]

When the mother was seen, she confirmed much of her son's story. She said, "This is very embarrassing, Doctor, and I was always afraid something like this might happen. And now it has really got out of hand. I know, because I've secretly followed him to see what he does when he goes outside dressed like a woman. Once I was afraid that he had seen me and knew what I was doing. This is terrible. What can be done? My husband and I are really very broad-minded [this refers to family nudity, mother dressing and bathing in front of her son, and so forth]. My son is such a good boy. If I looked nice, he'd tell me. He'd even advise me on what dress I'd look best in. Even if he doesn't say so, I can tell, because he gets that funny look in his eye. My husband isn't half as thoughtful. He wouldn't even know if I were dressed at all. I don't think he even cares."

[Here is a mother who secretly follows her son, observes his actions and is fully aware of his unnatural interests. But she does nothing about it and says nothing about it to him. There is even the definite possibility that the son has seen his mother following him and still nothing was said by her to him. This mother covertly followed her son, observed him dressed like a woman and failed to forbid such behavior immediately and unreservedly. Her actions revealed her complete awareness and acceptance of her son's perversion. Even if the son were not aware of her spying, he would sense her true feelings in the matter by innumerable other ways already noted (see Chap. 13). Here was not only maternal permission but actual maternal fostering of this bizarre behavior. This mother delights in her son's unusual interest in what she wears and even seeks her son's advice in such matters. She compares her son with her husband in a manner which need not and should not be. Father and son should not compete to see who can compliment mother best. The relationship between mother and son should be different from that between wife and husband. However, this mother is confused about this difference and thinks of her son in a way that should only be reserved for her husband. This in itself would be destructive enough to her son and serve to keep him functioning emotionally at the first romance stage of development. But she goes further and fosters his dressing and behaving like a woman. This is highly destructive to her son's manhood.]

The destructive nature of the mother's permissiveness in the way she reared her son was greatly clarified when she described her relationships with her own father. While going into detail about her father's violent temper and abusiveness, the mother spoke with few visible signs of emotion and, in fact, had a sweet smile of forebearance on her face. Her father was very abusive and had an extremely violent temper which would explode on the slightest provocation. On one occasion, the father threw a penknife at one of his daughters, cutting her on the shoulder. Another time, during one of his nightly violent arguments with his wife, the father ran all over the house after his terrified screaming wife brandishing an andiron. Fortunately, Pat's mother knew how to get around her father.

She seldom had to endure his cruelties, because she was a "goody-goody." Beyond that, her father, on special occasions, was very affectionate to his daughter, Pat's mother; even until her late 'teens, he held her on his lap, hugged her and kissed her. There was an unspoken understanding in the house, that the father went out with other women. The mother knew about this, as did the daughters, and the father knew that they knew. But nobody ever said anything about it. Pat's mother vividly remembered one occasion when she was passing a tavern late at night. She looked in and saw her father drunkenly embracing a neighbor woman. The father looked up and glared at her. Pat's mother, frightened, raced home. Never since had she mentioned this incident to anyone. Toward the end of her interview with the physician, Pat's mother stated, "My own parents fought continuously. I always sought a peace that they never had. I tried my best to take myself from their world and enter another when I married. If life hadn't been so good to me in giving me such a wonderful son, I don't know what I would have done. If it were not for my son, I would not be able to continue living with my husband."

[Pat's mother wanted from marriage everything that was missing in her parents' married life. However, the emotional inoculation she received as a child from her very confused relationship with her sadistic, philandering father affected for all time her attitudes toward men. Not surprisingly, her own married life was therefore a failure, and her mother-son relationship became a perversion. Although life was not unbearable so far as she was concerned, and although she was making a go of her marriage, her feelings beneath the surface had robbed her son of his manhood by nearly transforming him into a woman. In fact, as one stops to think about it, life was bearable, and the marriage was saved only because the mother could give vent to her hostility toward men through the destruction of her son. The vicarious gratification afforded this mother by the destruction of her son's masculinity was a sweet revenge upon her sadistic and philandering father. In this way, she could continue to live in an uneasy peace with her husband and herself.

[It is interesting that the two-faced behavior that existed between Pat's mother and her father was a repetition of the similar behavior between Pat himself and his mother. Father and daughter (and wife) were both aware of the philandering; mother and son were both aware of the transvestitism. And each knew of the other's awareness, but all the individuals concerned accepted this bizarre behavior without comment. Failure to react forthrightly when all concerned are aware of a perverted situation constitutes frank permission for such perversion. The reader might understandably wonder what sort of man her husband could be to permit this to occur. Knowing little about him other than what has already been mentioned, his own emotional stability should be seriously questioned.]

However, the problem of boys and men with lesser degrees of confusion regarding their sex is more prevalent than the rare cases of transvestitism. Thus, more common than boys and men who actually dress like women are the boys and the men who are passive and effeminate and might even choose occupations usually reserved for women. By this means, their confusion regarding masculinity and femininity may be constructively adapted to behavior that society will accept (see pp. 13, 14). The importance of this discussion of transvestitism, wherein the parental deviations are of extreme degree, lies in the fact that the same causative factors, operating only to a lesser degree, are almost the rule in the background of passive boys and men. These factors, so easily and vividly perceived in such a gross deviation like transvestitism, make it easier to recognize the same mechanisms when they are operative to a lesser extent and in a more subtle manner in the more common forms of the same general problem. Some of the closely related factors which are important in accounting for such passivity, be it greater or lesser in degree, are: a too-close relationship between son and mother; a mother's fostering femininity in her son; constant exposure to the example of his father's passivity; and the son's fear of a tyrannical father who hostilely competes with him. Among examples of such lesser degrees of passive men already mentioned are the fathers of the obese boy (Chap. 6) and the boy with asthma (Chap. 12).

In most cases, there is a blending of many of these varying factors.

The same kind of parental confusion can also exist in the backgrounds of girls and women as in those of boys and men. The same grotesque deviations and the same differences in degree (but not in type) result. Analogous to passive boys and men, girls and women who are aggressive and masculine often have backgrounds in which there has been an unnaturally close relationship between daughter and father (see Chap. 10). These girls and women have a lurking fear of inferiority to men. They must prove that there is no inferiority by continually competing with men on men's own grounds. "Anything you can do, I can do better." It is a protest against men and their presumed superiority. Women with such confusions about masculinity and femininity may tend to dress mannishly; act, walk and talk like men; tend to compete with men; and may even show a preference for occupations usually reserved for men.

CHAPTER 16

A Trail of Broken Hearts

The telephone rang. "Doctor, can you help my daughter? She's a nymphomaniac. I've known for a long time that she is loose with fellows. I can't stop her. I'm afraid she'll get pregnant and disgrace us all. You must help us. Please let me see you as soon as possible."

[Why the sudden urgency in seeking medical help when she has known of her daughter's difficulties for a long time? The mother has been unable to cope with this problem, and her chief concern at the present time is not the possible harm to her daughter but the possible shame to the family, including herself. She pleads, "You must help us," and not, "You must help her."]

The following day Mrs. N appeared at the physician's office. Although she was obviously a woman in her late forties, she was dressed like a young Hollywood movie actress. Tinted hair arranged neatly with bangs, generous use of make-up, bright-red fingernails, excessive use of perfume, and shoes with open toes and very high heels could not hide the fact that life had not been kind to her.

"I'm so glad you could see me so soon, Doctor. It's Delores, my daughter. We're worried she's going to do something foolish. She's boy crazy, running around wild, going with bad company . . . I don't see how she can be this way . . . my husband and I have always given her everything . . . why should she be interested in boys? We might not have much, Doctor, but we are decent, moral people. She's such a beautiful girl. She has my hair and eyes. I remember my uncle Bob telling me when she was only 2 years old that, 'All pretty girls get into trouble.' . . . Such a shame!"

153

As the interview progressed, it became clear that there were many parental factors at the root of the daughter's problem. The physician was not perturbed by any one incident, but the constant pattern of a series of events, all pointing in the same direction, left little doubt about the causative factors.

"Jack's [the husband's] mother lived with us when Delores was young. Grandma was never married, and Jack never saw his father. I've always felt sorry for that; you can't blame the child for what his mother does. But, I've always wondered if this family weakness might have come out in my own child. Once Delores asked me about her grandfather. I read in a book that a mother should always tell the truth to her children. I told Delores everything I knew; I told her not to ask Daddy about it because it would upset him."

[The mother has a dangerous fear. She is afraid that Delores will follow in the path of her paternal grandmother. Did she help Delores by telling her the whole truth? By telling her daughter about the illegitimacy she cast moral slurs upon the father, thus decreasing his stature in the child's eyes. Even more important, she was telling her daughter what could be and had been done in her own family. She was revealing an alternative to complete morality and thus was leaving a gaping hole in Delores' developing conscience. Illegitimacy because of bad heredity: another convenient scapegoat and, in this case, also permission for future similar acts by the daughter!]

"When Delores was 4, I caught her out in the street without any clothes on. I was terribly upset . . . ran out into the street, grabbed her by the arm and yanked her back into the house. I had told her never to do that. She knew that there are boys and strange men on the street, and little girls should be careful . . . if she did that then, what would she do later? I knew Grandma should never have lived with us."

[It should be recalled that children at that age have great interest in their bodies and at times innocently remove their clothes in public. Handled correctly with tact and with knowledge of what it really means, this behavior disappears of its own accord with the continued development of the child. The child learns from the parent that such things just are not done. However, Delores' mother was terribly upset by such behavior and feared many serious consequences (". . . boys and strange men on the street, and little girls should be careful . . . if she did that then, what would she do later?"). In fact, her fears were voiced even before this incident ("I had told her never to do that"), and the specific fear she had was that Delores would get into the same kind of trouble as her grandmother. Why should a mother who is comfortable in her role as a woman, wife and mother and loves, is loved and has been loved have such fears for a 4-year-old daughter? May she not be putting ideas into her daughter's head and inoculating the child with her own forbidden desires which she herself may not dare to express?]

". . . . Delores used to play doctor with a neighbor boy, Johnny, about the same age. She was very good about it . . . played in the house where I could see what was going on. They did it for years . . . a childhood infatuation. However, one time my mother-in-law caught them together; Delores was 8 then; she didn't have her periods yet, so there was nothing to worry about. Since then I've always reminded Delores of what she did and what a close call she had. Fortunately, we knew an unmarried girl with a baby; I warned Delores to be careful or she'd end up that way too. My husband says that in many ways Delores is just like me. He keeps reminding me of my past, what I did before I met him . . . I'm sorry I ever told him . . . that's just water under the bridge. I wish he'd shut up. He even brings it up in front of Delores. He knows how it upsets me. I get so angry. . . ."

[Playing doctor in front of the mother for many years. Is such obvious sexual play between children permissible only because it is done in the house under mother's watchful eyes? And, is not the mother encouraging this situation? Curiosity about their bodies is not unusual in healthy young children. In this particular instance, however, with the values attached to sex by this mother (and daughter), it would seem that such play permitted only under the mother's watchful eyes, and persisting over a long period of time, had become the means for this mother to derive vicarious enjoyment from the situation. What 8-year-old Delores does is permissible (and encouraged) as long as there is no fear of pregnancy. What a

distorted sense of values to instill into a child's developing conscience! This continual harping on pregnancy as if the prevention of illegitimate pregnancy were the sum total of one's
moral values! In the mother's mind it is not a question of
forbidding promiscuity; it is only a question of not becoming
pregnant.

[It might be conjectured that the father and the mother are
not getting along well together. The father's harping on his
wife's past betrays his faulty relationship with his wife and his
thinly disguised contempt and hostility for her. It not only
savagely undermines his wife's self-esteem but, being done in
the presence of the child, it destroys the mother in the child's
eyes and gives permission for the child to do what the mother
has already done. The father blames the mother for her earlier
moral laxity, while the mother flaunts the loose morals associated with her husband's origin.]

With the above information in mind, the physician asked
Mrs. N. about her own life, past and present. In order to introduce the subject as tactfully and as gently as possible, he
asked her about what she liked to read. With a little embarrassed laugh, Mrs. N. replied, "I wish I were living it and
not reading it, Doctor, but since you ask, I mostly read mag-
azines with stories about the private lives of actors and ac-
tresses, women in love . . . you know . . . the kind of things
we middle-aged women read . . . ever since I was a girl I've
read that kind of story. Delores does too. I guess she takes
after me . . . I guess you'd say I am oversexed. I suppose I
am."

However, Mrs. N.'s answers to the physician's further specific questioning convinced him beyond any doubt that she
was, on the contrary, a frigid woman, and had a totally un-
satisfactory physical adjustment in marriage. The physician had
seen many cases of promiscuous girls and boys who had frigid
mothers.

[Such mothers obtain some compensatory pleasure for their
own (sexual) difficulties through encouraging sexual overtones in the play and the behavior of their children. By the
parents' continued interest, permission and encouragement,
such play and behavior emerge as outright sexual promiscuity.

Seeing this, the parent obtains fulfillment of his or her own deep desires, but, outwardly, to the world, the parent appears to be horrified. All this has been accomplished without either the parent or child realizing her own unwittingly engendered complicity in the matter.]

The physician now had many questions about Delores' father, but since the father would not come to be studied separately, the physician had to be satisfied by obtaining what information he could from the mother. "Well, as I said, Doctor, our house is very small. Our bedroom, Jack's and mine, is separated from Delores' by the bathroom. We keep the doors open all the time. Naturally, we can't have much privacy in such a small house, and it doesn't bother us anyway . . . Delores has seen her father taking a shower many times, and it doesn't bother them. As a matter of fact, until she was 10, she always took Sunday morning showers with her father. She was a Daddy's girl . . . she never came to my bed. Always wanted to sleep with her Daddy . . . go any place he went and even do exercises with him. He's a 'bug' on physical culture . . . thinks a lot of his appearance and figure. They still do it, both in their underwear. You should see them. It's really cute.

"Why do you ask me all these questions, Doctor? What do you want to know? Do you think Jack is the cause of Delores' troubles? Come to think of it, Delores has been asking me why Daddy always has to go into the bathroom when she's bathing. She said, 'He always finds some excuse like bringing in a fresh cake of soap, clean towels or just to fix the window.' Is that wrong, Doctor? I wonder. Maybe something is wrong with Jack. . . ."

[Again, many examples of unhealthy and sexually charged relationships in this family, this time between father and daughter. The mother wonders whether something is wrong with her husband. The unfortunate fact is that all three, father, mother and daughter, are deeply involved in this unfolding tragedy.]

At the conclusion of the interview, Mrs. N. looked at the doctor and said, "I don't know what all these questions have to do with Delores' looseness with boys. Frankly, I don't see

how all this dressing and bathing business can have anything
to do with Delores' trouble. All my friends do it. They're all
modern . . . none of this mid-Victorian prudishness."

[Does the fact that something is widespread necessarily make
it healthy? It is well known that cancer, heart disease and
tuberculosis are widespread, for example, but it is also well
known that these represent disease and not health. It is
agreed that the type of parent-child behavior referred to by
Mrs. N. is widespread. It has been shown by many complete
and well-documented studies, in some instances extending
over a period of years, that such behavior is entirely unhealthy. This modern frankness often represents unsatisfied
emotional needs, disguised hatreds, glaring conscience defects,
denied passions and perverted sexuality of the parents. All
those warped passions and distorted forms of hate seethe
malignantly beneath the surface, constantly poisoning the
feelings, the thoughts and the actions of the unsuspecting
parent. In many, many ways, the unfortunate parent unwittingly spews these poisons onto his child from earliest infancy.
The child cannot escape. The same marked passions and distorted forms of hate mar the child. This is a tragedy of life.
Unless interrupted, it will go on and on, infecting and doom-
ing each successive generation with the poisons of the old.
With such destructive causes and effects, how can the "modern frankness" referred to by Mrs. N. be considered healthy
regardless of how widespread such behavior may be and how
numerous the statistics to prove its prevalence?]

The physician realized that the basic problems were deep
below the surface and that neither father nor mother was even
aware of their existence. The physician, seeing that just
touching lightly on these problems with his questions aroused
much tension in Mrs. N., pushed things no further at this
time. He asked Mrs. N. if he could see Delores. The physician was very anxious to see her, but he was somewhat taken
aback to see a short, fat girl who took little pride in her personal appearance and chewed gum incessantly. She wore a
plain black dress which, by its tight fit, only emphasized her
uncomeliness. The lipstick, as applied, made her mouth seem
unattractively large and crooked. The poorly applied heavy

layers of powder and rouge on her face could not conceal the many pimples. Delores spoke in a quiet, rather shy monotone. She seemed quite indifferent when describing her many boy friends. She confirmed quietly and without apparent emotion her promiscuity. When asked why she did these things, she answered, "I don't know." Why did she get into such a jam? "I guess I was just born that way." In a dull and lifeless manner, Delores confirmed all that her mother had said. But she was not the beautiful, interesting girl her mother had led the physician to believe. She was only a frightened, unhappy and lonely girl.

CHAPTER 17

Consider Your Child's Emotions Before and After Surgery

"This is a great age we live in. If it were not for this heroic surgery, we'd have lost our child. We're so lucky to have been able to get the finest surgeon in the country. That man really knows his business. To think of what he can do!"

The technical skill of the surgeon is frequently extolled as being of heroic proportions. Such praise is entirely understandable. But too often it is forgotten by all concerned that it is not the surgeon who is heroic but rather the child (or adult patient) who must undergo surgery.

To the child, an operation is an operation. He does not know whether it is a serious one or a simple one, nor does he care. To the child, it is a frightening situation. Since most of the surgery done in childhood is not done to relieve pain, the child often cannot even see the reason for the surgery. For example, in this category one finds tonsillectomies, circumcisions and operations on the eyes, the bones or the joints to correct deformities with which a child may be born. Suddenly, with little apparent reason, he is whisked from his home to something entirely new. He finds himself in a strange room or in a children's ward filled with many noisy, crying children, many as fearful as himself. He sees children swathed in bandages, encased in plaster casts or lying within oxygen tents. He sees other children lying motionlessly on their backs, with large tubes coming out of their bodies and attached to complicated, noisy machines that suck out blood and fluid from the body. He sees other children being stuck with needles to take blood out of the body while adults hold the screaming child still. Other children, bound down so they cannot move, have needles which are placed in their arms or legs and attached to long tubes which lead to bottles of blood or fluids held high above the bed. He sees white-uniformed nurses give injections to frightened, screaming children. He sees men all in white with caps and masks hiding all but their eyes hurriedly wheel back on giant stretchers children who breathe noisily but lie very still. He sees nurses put rubber tubes in children's noses and throats and suck out fluids with gurgling machines. Curious new odors of antiseptics, ether, bedpans and draining body fluids pervade the air. But this is the children's wing of the hospital. In spite of all the new and frightening experiences, the basic nature of children asserts itself. They must explore, play, laugh and get into mischief. Happiness, fear, curiosity and suffering are all intertwined. For practical purposes, whether the child patient be placed in a single room, a semiprivate room or an open ward, the same general situation holds true. Wherever he may be, the child is always interested in and fully aware of what goes on about him.

The child has been separated from his parents and abruptly transferred from the peace and quiet of his home to the children's wing of the hospital. He may adjust very readily to the new situation and, if able, will shortly be playing merrily with the others, or, his initial loneliness and fear may increase, and no amount of consoling by the nurses and other children can help. In this latter situation the child has the same background of helpless dependency already seen in the school phobia (see Chap. 11). Children who have an excessive fear of separation from their parents will usually not benefit to the same degree as the healthy child when the physician and parents discuss the situation with them prior to hospitalization. Such children adapt themselves less readily and less completely to the new situation.

How should the child be told of the surgery that is planned, and when should he be told? As soon as the physician has decided when the surgery will be performed, plans can be made for telling the child. A young child, up to 3 or 4 years of age, has a poor concept of time, past or future. A trip to the zoo that occurred 1 month previously may be referred to as having occurred "yesterday." His concept of the future is always in terms of the immediate future, in terms of hours or days; the distant future usually has no meaning. "I want what I want when I want it." The child cannot keep his past and future tenses straight when he talks; his speech is most often in the present tense. He understands only the here and now. Therefore, one explains the planned surgery to a child of this age shortly before the surgery is to be done. This is a matter of days and not weeks or months. Of course, an older child should be prepared earlier. Therefore, should the physician decide that immediate emergency surgery is necessary, the child should be told. The feelings and the respect that the parents have for the physician as a healer are communicated to the child. The physician's kind and firm attitude will go a long way in ensuring an emotionally smooth hospitalization provided that the parents uphold him throughout. If the parents show any exaggerated concern or agitation or indulge in any histrionics, the child will naturally also become extremely fearful. At such a point, it may be very difficult for the doctors and the nurses to manage the situation.

If surgery is to be done in the distant future, the physician and the parents need not discuss the situation with the child at the first visit unless the child is old enough. This would apply, for example, to an operation for an uncomplicated rupture which is certainly not an emergency. The planned surgery should be discussed with the child at the appropriate time.

The child might want to talk about the expected surgery, and it is highly beneficial that he do so. Young children have many ideas, right, wrong, real, make-believe and exaggerated, about what the surgery will entail. This may be more evident in their play and dreams than in anything they actually say. Again, when appropriate, simple information, emphasizing the good and not the frightening, should correct the many apprehensions and misconceptions that the child has picked up from his playmates—and all too frequently from his parents. It is better that such information be given in answer to the child's specific questions. If the parent is attentive, he will immediately understand what the child is trying to say. Quite often the fear of the planned surgery is so overwhelming that the child will not dare talk about it or ask about it directly. But the parents should know their child well enough to recognize the hints, the indirect questions and the veiled fears when they arise. The parents will not help the child by repeatedly bringing up the subject of surgery when they wish to discuss it. This has nothing to do with the child's needs but frequently is only an expression of the parents' own confusion, fear, and need to talk about the surgery. This, then, under the guise of modern frankness and desire to make things clear to the child, becomes another way by which the parents communicate their confusions and fears to the child.

Whatever the physician and the parents tell the child should be simple, honest and in a language that the child can easily understand. There is no need to go into a long detailed explanation of what will be done. It is not a question of, "We will cut here" or "We will cut this out or that" and so on. Emphasize, in general terms, the constructive and positive: "We will fix it"; "You will be able to play with your friends again"; "We will make it better"; "The pain will go away." However, in the preparation of the child, he should be told honestly that, following his operation, there will be some pain, but that it will stay for only a short time and then go away.

If it is expected that a child will have a dressing or a plaster cast applied to some part of his body during surgery, he should be told of this specifically prior to surgery. He should be reassured that the dressing or cast is another part of the treatment that is necessary to make him better. For example, it is a terrifying experience for a child to awaken from eye surgery and find a dressing over his eyes which completely blinds him. If he had not been prepared for this prior to surgery, it will be extremely difficult to allay his fright.

Equally important as these other factors in preparing a child for surgery is the preparation of the child for anesthesia. It should be emphasized that before the operation, he will be given medicine to make him sleep so that he will feel no pain during the surgery. This medicine, it should be stated, will make him sleep until the operation is finished. Shortly before surgery, the physician who will give the anesthesia should tell the child in simple terms that he can understand, the method by which he will be put to sleep. This interview not only gives the child information which he may need to allay his fears but also introduces him to the physician who will anesthetize him. In this way, at the time of anesthesia, the child will not suddenly be faced with a stranger whom he may fear and mistrust.

It is misguided kindness, plain stupidity, deceit and even brutality to lie to the child. All too often the child is told some silly story rather than the truth. For example, he may be told that he is going to the store for a new pair of shoes and then finds himself in the hospital getting prepared for surgery or in the doctor's office getting a "shot." Similarly, telling a child that there will be no pain in anticipated painful surgery, painful change of dressings or getting a shot is as stupid and brutal and unrealistic.

When the child goes to the hospital, this may well be the first time he is leaving his home or his parents. It is helpful to give him something to bridge the gap, a reminder of home and parents. Most young children have a favorite toy or a tattered blanket to which they are very attached and with which they must go to bed every night. Why should not the child take this toy or blanket with him to the hospital? By all means the parents owe it to their child to accompany him personally to the ward or the room in which he will be and to introduce him to the doctors and the nurses who will be with him. The child is not just a tonsil or appendix to be removed; he is a complete individual, however tiny, helpless and inarticulate he may be. He has his own feelings and rights which must be respected by the grown-ups.

Any violation of these feelings and rights of the child, no matter how sympathetically and justifiably presented to him, will be received by him with some element of indignation. Emotionally considered, the child will view any injection, insertion of a tube into his mouth or rectum or any operation, as an assault on his body. Something painful is being done to him with little or no consideration for his feelings in the matter. This reaction is almost invariably present in any child, the "good patient" who is quiet and almost obsequiously cooperative or the noisy protesting child who fusses constantly and raises pandemonium in the hospital.

A word about the "good patient." Just because the child is quiet, noncomplaining and obsequiously obedient does not mean that he is escaping the emotional stresses associated with the situation. Very often this only means that he is afraid to express himself. He is too aware of his helplessness. But the tensions are there and build up at a greater rate because of this inability to give vent to his feelings. An explosion, when it does occur, may be even greater and more startling because of its unexpectedness. The proud statement: "He took it like a man!" may mean not that the child was brave but that the observer was quite stupid and completely calloused to the feelings and the needs of the child.

If the Teddy bear or blanket means so much to the child that it is almost a part of him, other things that belong to the child are equally, if not more, important. Such items as a wristwatch, a pocketbook, a cowboy belt, or eyeglasses are so closely associated with the child in the parent's mind and in the child's mind that they are a part of him. The child thinks of these things as not only belonging to his own person and body but has the same kind of affection for them that grown-ups might have for one another. This is exactly the same feeling that the child has for his own body and its parts, his arms and legs and general appearance. In a word, he has highly personal and charged feelings for each part of his body and all the parts together, his total image. These feelings are just there; he takes them for granted; he is not even aware of them. This applies as strongly for body characteristics which may be beautiful as for those which might be ugly but which the child has learned to accept as an integral part of himself from long contact. For example, the child looks upon a birthmark as a part of himself, no matter how large and unsightly or how much it sets him apart from the world around him. He will have mixed feelings about such an unsightly part of his body. On the one hand, the birthmark is his to be cherished as a badge of his individuality; on the other hand, however, the birthmark is an unsightly blemish at which people may stare and it may even repulse some. These same feelings apply to visible scars, burns and other longstanding acquired blemishes and disabilities that the child has learned to accept as a part of him as a result of having had them a long time. He cherishes as old intimate friends his body and all its parts, inside and outside, in health and disease. These feelings later develop into the pride that men or women take in their personal appearance, neatness and grooming. In some individuals these normal feelings become exaggerated, and personal appearance becomes an end in itself. These people are extremely and obviously vain; they take a morbid interest in every change in their bodies. They are the devotees of physical culture.

Any surgery or injury which alters the physical appearance and the function of the body or any of its parts, particularly if visible, will naturally upset the child. How well the child adjusts to these changes depends on how well the child was managed by the grown-ups before, during and after the operation or the treatment and on the importance that the child and his parents attach to the changed part.

Was the child tricked or told lies when he was taken to the hospital? Have the parents previously threatened the child with taking him to the physician, the dentist or the hospital if the child was not good? Does the mother fear some dire effects from surgery despite the physician's repeated reassurances, fears that the child readily senses? Do the parents lack confidence in the physician, another feeling which the child readily perceives? Have x-ray pictures, enemas, changes of dressings and other procedures been done in the hospital without proper respect for the child's feelings?

Hospitalization for the child, as already mentioned, frequently represents the first separation of the child from the home and the parents. Certainly it is one of the few times when he is to be placed with complete strangers. If at the time of separation there is the same mutually unbearable anxiety between parent and child that was seen in school phobias (and for the same basic reasons; see Chap. 11), such tension gets out of control and is more destructive to the child than anything in the current situation. The hospital and everything connected with it becomes the convenient scapegoat for the parent's and the child's own deep-rooted unresolved tensions. A very common example is the mother who fears all sorts of horrible complications and insists that she or her husband stay with her child on an all-day and all-night vigil. The physician knows such parents well. They ask countless and repeated questions about the dangers of putting the child to sleep, serious drug and blood transfusion reactions, the child's chances of surviving the operation and the possibility of complications, mutilations and unsightly scars. It is a hopeless task for the physician to reassure and explain. Then, despite the complete technical success of the operation and treatment, such parents, in the presence of the operated child and other children, dwell at great lengths on the narrow escape from death that the child had, his profuse bleeding during surgery, exactly what and how much was removed and a detailed and frightening description of each phase of the treatment before and after surgery. The surgery has been technically successful, but the child and parents, for reasons in the family situation alone, have had a great emotional upheaval. This and subsequent emotional disturbances, expected in such a situation anyway, are blamed on the surgery. The surgical procedure, the hospitalization and the necessary treatments have become convenient scapegoats for future emotional disturbances. Such disturbances may be precipitated by surgery, but they might occur anyway even if the surgery were not performed. Another precipitating event might be found.

During the first romance stage, the child first becomes aware of the physical differences between boys and girls and men and women. Parents who have watched and listened to their children know that boys and girls at this stage of development attach great importance to these differences. However, the girl might also wonder why she is different. She might wonder if she had been made originally like a boy and if something had been done to her to change her. Many little girls even wish that they were like boys. In fact, some little girls, because of parental confusion in this matter, never get over this wish and grow up to be tomboys, competing with boys at play and, later in life, with men at work (see p. 151).

Because of the special significance that the child attaches to the characteristics of sex during the first romance stage, he becomes especially concerned at this age with any procedure, surgical or otherwise, directed to the genitals or any other part of the body which the child may unwittingly associate with this region. Common everyday examples are dental work and haircuts. However, as important, even if less frequent, are procedures done on the nose, the throat and the mouth. At this age, circumcision of the boy and catheterization (insertion of a tube into the bladder) of the boy or the girl can be especially fearsome. If such a procedure can be deferred until a later stage of development, it is advisable to do so. If it must be done during this stage, even greater preparation and precautions are necessary.

Boys and girls also attach special significance to particular parts of their bodies for reasons learned from their parents. The violinist's son will be particularly careful of his hands. The hairdresser's little girl might be more concerned about her hair than is the case with other children. The extremely pretty little girl, praised by proud parents, doting relatives and even absolute strangers for her beauty, will be especially disturbed by anything that may disfigure her face. The swimming champion's son will be overly concerned about the muscles of his arms. It will be obvious that in these situations an injury or operation to that part of the body which has special significance to the child (and his parents) will be more upsetting emotionally than an operation or injury to another part of the body.

In considering the effects of surgery, injury and hospitalization (removal from home and parents) on the child during the first romance stage, another important factor must be discussed. It will be remembered that during this stage, the boy competes with his father for his mother's affection while the girl competes with her mother for her father's affection. At times, the boy has the half-formed desire to have his mother to himself while the girl has similar feelings toward her father.

However, as in many other situations where the emotions are involved, their feelings are mixed. The little child cannot have his cake and eat it too. Both the boy and the girl realize that these wishes of getting rid of the parent of the same sex are rather far-fetched and impractical. The little boy fully realizes that he really needs his father, while the little girl feels the same way toward her mother. In addition to this obvious dependency, the little boy, as noted earlier, wants to grow up to be like his father, while the little girl wants to be like her mother. Dependency on and desire to imitate the parent of the same sex seesaws with the hostile feelings toward this parent. In the emotionally healthy child, this inner contest of feelings is decided in favor of peace with the parent of the same sex. The boy loves and admires his father and desires to imitate him—"Like father, like son." The contest is resolved similarly for the girl. At this point, each is ready to leave the first romance stage and progress onward. However, a residue of the former conflict remains. No peace is perfect. From time to time, differences will arise between the father and son and the mother and daughter. The never-quite-extinguished embers of the old rivalry temporarily burst forth again into flames. In a healthy situation, these differences will be solved; there will be peace again. As a result of such rivalry and associated outbursts, in the knowledge that each really loves and respects the other, and should love and respect the other, each will have understandable feelings of guilt. Each is sorry for his part in all this. The peace is more uneasy, the guilt is greater, and the outbursts threaten to get out of control—and sometimes do—when the relationship between parent and child is emotionally unhealthy.

These feelings of guilt bring with them the fear, the expectation and sometimes even the desire for punishment to assuage the guilt. This is no less true of the child than it is of the adult. Such a child fears, expects and sometimes may even desire punishment. Suddenly he is faced with surgery, injury, or separation from his parents (hospitalization). He readily, although mistakenly, concludes that this is his punishment for his angry rivalry with the parent of the same sex. In addition to this natural or exaggerated angry rivalry and guilt, the child is quite angry with his parents for permitting surgery and separation from home.

The special significance attached to the physical differences between the sexes and the high point of child-parent rivalry and the consequent guilt for these angry feelings are most intense during the first romance stage. For these reasons, emotional disturbances resulting from surgery, injury, or hospitalization are most likely to occur during the first romance stage. That is why the physician prefers, if at all possible, to do no surgery at this time, especially if such surgery is to be in the genital area or a part of the body which the child may unwittingly associate with this region. For example, circumcision, repair of ruptures, catheterizations and specialized plastic surgery of the genital area should be postponed, if at all possible, during this stage.

Four-year-old little Louise has just returned home from the hospital following removal of her appendix. Louise is very eager to show everybody her tummy. In her play she is the nurse, and all her dolls have become patients with "sore tummies." She betrays the feelings that she must have had in the hospital by re-enacting her own hospitalization. She rather forcefully slaps the doll down, gives the doll an injection with a pencil and then gives 3 or 4 more injections. "There, now, you be quiet and be good, or I'll give you more injections. Stop crying for Mommy; I'm here. I'm a nurse, and I'll make you feel better." Louise then cuddles the doll in her arms.

Despite the excellent management of Louise by the parents, the physicians and the nurses in this emergency, Louise still had an upsetting experience. The injections hurt her; her abdomen was sore; and she missed her parents. Naturally, Louise did not like the injections she received, and no matter how skillfully given and how kind the nurse, a "shot" is a "shot," and it hurts. Therefore, in her heart, Louise had understandably mixed feelings about the nurses. To her way of thinking, they were mean and they caused pain; but they were also kind and friendly when they fed her, rubbed her back, bathed her and sympathetically cared for her many other needs. Louise revealed these mixed feelings when she, while playing nurse, handled her doll roughly and gave repeated shots and when she said, as the nurse did, "Stop crying for Mommy. I'm here. I'll make you better," and then cuddled her "patient." In her play with the dolls, Louise reenacted her own operation and her upsetting emotional experience. In this way she got rid of much of the emotional tension associated with her surgery.

Louise's mother chuckled and told the physician, "Louise did just beautifully. Her only trouble was the first two nights home from the hospital. She had nightmares both times. She dreamed of being chased by a big black wolf with very sharp teeth. But, she's all over it now . . . now she has set her heart on becoming a nurse for little girls."

[More proof of the fact that hospitalization and surgery were upsetting. Louise is pursued by a wolf who in the young child's mind is mean and terribly frightening. For example, recall the common children's stories of "Little Red Riding Hood" and "The Three Little Pigs and The Big Bad Wolf." The wolf had very sharp teeth with which to cut Louise—as the surgeon did. Her dreams are an expression of the fears she had. And by being able to express fears, even in dreams, one may relieve, at least in part, the tension engendered by these fears. The recurrent nightmares—as well as Louise's play with her dolls—acted as an escape valve for the tension built up by her recent experiences in the hospital. The triumph of good over bad in Louise's mixed feelings about the nurses is revealed by her desire to become a nurse herself.]

It is understood, of course, that all adults concerned with the care of the child (parents, nurses, laboratory and x-ray technicians, and physicians of all the specialties that make up the medical team) should deal with the child with sincerity, kindness and understanding.

It is not generally understood that in the past few decades contributions from medicine and its many allied fields have been responsible for reducing the dangers of surgery. Surgical procedures which were very dangerous, impossible or could not even have been considered a few decades ago are now commonplace in most large hospitals as a result of these important and far-reaching contributions from the surgeon's associates in and out of medicine. This newer knowledge has made possible a hospitalization during which more can be done for the patient with greater safety and with milder and shorter emotional upheavals.

When the child goes to the dentist, unusual skill in handling the child's emotions must be shown by both parent and dentist. Here is a situation where the child must hold his mouth open while fully aware of what is happening. Nowhere is the child's co-operation and confidence more important. The fact that dentists can do their work under such trying circumstances, shows their great skill and success in dealing with children's everyday fears.

CHAPTER 18

Emotional Problems of the Handicapped Child

In the last chapter it was shown how the child "cherishes as old intimate friends, his body and all its parts, inside and outside, in health and disease." The handicapped child sees himself as having certain differences from other children. These differences are an integral part of his body. His deformity or internal handicap is as much a part of him in his mind's eye as the presence of 2 legs is to another child. It is as difficult for the child with the weak left arm to think of himself as not having this disability as it is for the nondisabled child to think of himself as not having 2 arms. Every reader will immediately recognize this basic principle in the grown-up world when he remembers how different grandmother looked to others—and to herself—with her new eyeglasses or new false teeth. Grandmother had learned to think of herself and see herself as she had been before. She had to adjust to her new appearance. At first she not only looked different to herself and to others but she also felt different. Part of her changed feelings were in response to the changed reactions that others may have had toward her. Similarly, the child, in his own mind's eye, sees himself as having a certain makeup, whether he has any disability or not, whether his deformities have been present from birth or acquired and whether they alter his appearance externally or are internal and only alter his life habits.

Defects which alter the external appearance of the child have a great influence on his emotional life. Similarly, defects in the child greatly influence the emotions of the parents. Fre-

175

quently, this initial response by the parents and their resulting attitudes will determine in great measure how well the child will adjust to his handicap. In such a situation a completely new vital and disturbing factor has been introduced into the family setting. Not only the child himself but also his parents and the other children cannot help being affected. In such an upsetting situation, following such a severe blow to their feelings, the parents and the other children need as much understanding and emotional support as does the child who is sick. Frequently, a little time spent with these distraught and frightened parents, recognizing their feelings as human beings, will help soften the blow and help pave the way for a realistic and healthy adjustment to the handicap. In this way both the handicapped child and his family will be better prepared for the vicissitudes that lie ahead.

This reaction of the child to his own body is influenced in large measure by the reaction of society, his family and friends to his defect. A noticeable defect may seriously impair function and handicap the child physically and yet not leave him emotionally crippled. On the other hand, a child with a radical alteration in his physical appearance might have little change in function (the parts work as well as ever), but he may be seriously crippled emotionally. For example, with the increased attention given in recent years to the problem of poliomyelitis, the public in general has learned to think of these people as having a disability which is unfortunately disabling but nevertheless common and permits them to function in our society in spite of their impaired ability to use their arms or legs as other people do. For example, their adjustment to society is made easier by the more lenient and understanding attitudes of the parents and the public at large. To show how important the feelings of others are in determining a patient's emotional adjustment, consider the case of the child who has received a severe burn of the face following a home accident. Unfortunately, this tragic accident might cause horrible scars and disfigurement of his face. The child has no eyebrows; the mouth is a thin slit; there is no nose in the usual sense—only a hole for each nostril; the skin is a twisted, distorted mass of white scar tissue; only the eyes seem to be alive in this masklike immobile distorted face. This is the full extent of the child's physical handicap. His brain can function as before; he can walk, run, grasp and lift as before. He can bite, chew and swallow food as others can. But he is a complete emotional cripple; he must have much medical help (psychiatric treatment as well as plastic surgery). Society is repulsed by him; he shuns society because he is ashamed. If there have been emotional disturbances in the previous child-parent relationship, the child's problems become more difficult. The disability activates any emotional disturbances that previously had only simmered beneath the surface. The unfortunate parents' ability to manage the situation may be made more difficult by their memory of the circumstances surrounding the accident.

Other deformities with varying degrees of accompanying disability and problems peculiar to the deformity and to the circumstances surrounding it are cerebral palsy, birthmarks, amputations, clubbed foot, deafness, blindness, harelip, cleft palate, crooked teeth, chronic eczema, deformities resulting from broken bones, brain injuries following accidents and permanent disabilities resulting from any injuries. Occasionally, permanent or temporary deformities and disabilities will result from surgery necessary to save life.

Up to this point, the emotional effects of obviously visible physical deformities have been discussed. There are many diseases occurring deep within the body with few if any obvious visible deformities, but with marked effects on the child's ability to adjust to life, physically and emotionally. For example, the patient with diabetes has a disease that is difficult even for a physician to detect without a complete examination and laboratory studies. Such a patient appears to be completely normal only because of diet and daily injections of insulin. By the regimen of careful dieting, daily preparation of sterile syringes and needles, daily self-injection of insulin, routine frequent examination of her urine and regular visits to the physician, such an individual is repeatedly reminded that she is different from other people. She has been taught that the spectres of insulin reactions (from too much insulin relative to her diet and exercise) and diabetic coma (from too little insulin relative to her diet and exercise) hang over her. She further knows that she must take extraordinary precautions to prevent and treat infections and to care for any cuts and bruises no matter how trivial. She knows from long experience that infections can run rampant, wounds may heal slowly and, in the presence of infections, her diabetes may go completely out of control and require hospitalization. This patient has learned to live with these disabilities. They are as much a part of her as the color of her hair and the shape of her nose. One may not think that the color of one's hair or the shape of one's nose is the most attractive, but they are one's own hair color and nose shape. They must be accepted for what they are.

Other diseases within the body which chiefly affect function rather than external appearance are epilepsy, tuberculosis, congenital heart disease, rheumatic heart disease, some thyroid diseases, some blood diseases, some results of brain fever and some chronic intestinal, kidney and liver diseases. From his own life-experiences, each patient with these various diseases knows that he cannot respond to the problems of everyday living as others do. These children are forever answering countless embarrassing questions about the reasons for their inability to do one thing or another. The classmates of the child with congenital heart disease know only that Sally looks no different from themselves; yet Sally does not go to gym class. Willie at 8 years of age looks the picture of health; he "daydreams" a lot in school; he has one form of epilepsy. John is rather thin, but how many 11-year-old boys are thin? John tires very easily and cannot keep up with the others. His parents discourage too violent play, because he has a long-standing kidney disease.

In each of these latter examples the child does not appear to be particularly different from healthy children. Yet he is sick with a disease that imposes severe limitations upon his behavior. If in the excitement of play, work or anger, the child were to violate these limitations, his body might quickly make him aware of his transgression and rebel. Unlike the children with obvious visible deformities who are conscious of and dependent upon the reactions of other people in general, these children, without obvious visible deformities, are much more dependent upon the fine shades of parent-child relationships and the often subtle attitudes of their parents to their disease.

These children with concealed defects are particularly vulnerable to a disturbed relationship with their parents. The child's disability becomes a convenient and pivotal point around which the underlying emotional tensions of the parent and the child can come to the surface. For example, at one extreme is the oversolicitous parent who insists on marked curtailment of the child's activities when such curtailment is not warranted by the degree of the child's disability. Such a child believes that he is far more crippled than he really is. At the other extreme is the overindulgent parent who permits activities of a dangerous degree not warranted by the child's disability. Neither the oversolicitous nor the overindulgent parent is acting appropriately in the situation described. These parents act as they do because of basic unresolved emotional problems in themselves of which they are not even aware. And, the unfortunate child's disability can become the convenient escape-hatch through which these parental feelings bubble up to the surface.

Johnny is 9 years old and has epilepsy. His attacks occur only one to two times a year since the physician placed him on certain medicines for his illness many years ago. However, Johnny's mother is oversolicitous. He cannot play with other boys without her repeated advice to take it easy and without her repeated admonitions to go into the house and rest. At the first sneeze, Johnny is put to bed, and the doctor is called. After the doctor has examined Johnny and found nothing wrong ("He just happened to sneeze"), the mother still feels that she must keep Johnny in bed 24 hours and insist on glass after glass of hot lemonade. Each time Johnny sniffles, his mother is terrified; what will it do to the epilepsy? Each time the physician sees Johnny, she asks the same questions: Can the epilepsy lead to mental deficiency? Is there any sign of this in Johnny? The physician has told her repeatedly and emphatically that there is no evidence at all of this condition in Johnny, nor is there any reason at all to fear that this may occur in Johnny's case. The mother knows better; she is convinced that Johnny will become mentally defective; she has heard stories, and she knows. Because of frequent absences from classes resulting from his mother's overwhelming fear, Johnny has been left back twice in school. This has only proved to the mother that she is right. She sees this as confirmation that Johnny, despite the doctor's denials, is really not too bright. She goes back and forth with her son to and from school. He cannot go anywhere without her tagging along. "Poor Johnny! He must suffer so! Why must he be punished this way?" The drug treatment of Johnny's epileptic attacks has been highly successful, but Johnny has a greater, more incapacitating problem. He cannot resist the constant bombardment of his mother's fears and overprotectiveness. Johnny mirrors his mother's sick feelings and fears. He, like his mother, is also firmly convinced that he has a shameful stigma, that he is completely different from other children, that he cannot enjoy life and that eventually something terrible must happen to him. In a way, and understandably, Johnny is angry at the world and its people because this has happened to him. "Why me, and not the others?" Johnny, knowing nothing else, has no choice. He can only accept this role that his mother presents to him. She is forever keeping him young. And in Johnny's own mind's eye, he sees himself as an epileptic who cannot enjoy life, who is severely incapacitated and to whom something terrible must happen eventually. He awaits the future with dread.

For reasons repeatedly described in previous chapters, this mother's adjustment to her father and to men in general, including her husband and son, was totally unhealthy. Laughingly Johnny's mother, Mrs. O., described her father as "a boarder in the house." She said her father was aloof and distant. He never showed any warmth or feeling and seldom spoke to his wife or daughter, Johnny's mother. He never remembered their birthdays or bought them presents. Mrs. O.'s relationship with her own mother was similarly lacking in any true warmth. Later in her 'teens Mrs. O. vowed that she would marry a man who would love and be kind to her, and she also vowed that she would love and be kind to her

own children. Never having received love, Mrs. O., in a
tragedy often repeated in life, suffered severe impairment
in her ability to give love. Her search for the love that she
missed in childhood failed—as it so often does in such circumstances. Her concept of love was distorted by her early
unhealthy relationship with her parents. She could be at-
tracted only to someone with a similarly distorted concept
of love. Her relationship with her husband and son was
doomed to be an outgrowth of her early unhealthy relationship with her father. She failed to find what she had missed
as a child. She married a man 20 years older than herself who
died shortly after Johnny's birth. When Johnny was born,
Mrs. O. dedicated herself to her son. Here would be her
chance to shower someone close to her with all the love and
kindness that she never had a chance to show. "All she needs
is to get married and have children." The naked tragedy is
that Mrs. O. received so little love that she had little to give
in return. She could give her son only that distorted facsimile
of love that she knew.

Her exaggerated fears represent her own confusions about
her role as a mother. As a mother, she knows that she should
love, and she really wants to love. Consciously, she desires
to give what she missed. If one were to ask Mrs. O. about this
she would state emphatically that she wants to love her son
and actually does love him: and she would be telling the truth
as she knows it. She is not even aware of her underlying
feelings of anger toward men specifically (and people in
general) stemming from her own highly disturbed parent-
daughter relationship. If Mrs. O. were told that she has deep
underlying anger which is not apparent on the surface, she
would be flabbergasted, even offended. She would deny that
any anger exists, on the surface or deep within her. She would
insist again that there is only love, and again she would be
telling the truth as she knows it. But this anger, inapparent to
her, is there and masquerades in a great variety of forms. At
times these facades are so far removed from the original anger
that produced them that the connecting link between the two
is completely submerged from view. In an effort to deny this
hostility to herself, her child and the world, she substitutes a

caricature of behavior that on the surface is the complete opposite of her deep-lying feelings. She has exaggerated fears (phobias), overprotectiveness, exaggerated protestations and demonstrations of love and obsessive preoccupation with trivialities. Although Mrs. O. does not fully understand her deeply hidden hostile feelings, she is dimly aware of them, and they affect her every action and emotion in a way that she does not even recognize. Her vague stirrings of angry emotions cannot rise to the surface without the danger of her being shattered by the unleashed rage. The parent with these deep painfully hostile feelings of hate develops certain symptoms which barricade her from an awareness of these seething emotions. Her symptoms are absolutely necessary to check her rage and preserve some sort of emotional balance. These symptoms are overprotectiveness and inappropriate concern for the child. She keeps these hatreds concealed from the world and herself by the appearance of these extreme protestations of love, concern and protection. These sick ideas and her exaggerated behavior serve to stunt and warp her son's emotional growth. He is enslaved in a state of abject dependency on his mother with all the same irrational and exaggerated fears that have barred his mother from happiness. These methods of containing her anger have become the instruments of her hate, the instruments for the destruction of her son. These symptoms that conceal her anger have become in fact the means of venting her hate. This is a boomerang. And neither victim, mother or son, understands the role that each plays in this tragedy.

Naturally, the mother who has this deep underlying hate also has deep underlying feelings of guilt. Her impaired ability to love when she knows she should but cannot love only increases her guilt. Her normal common-sense precautions become exaggerated into a reign of terror. Were her child to be hurt or develop a disability accidentally or otherwise, and were the mother at fault or not, it would only bring her intense feelings of guilt to the surface. The mother who already feels guilty will become highly disturbed out of all proportion to her situation. However, an emotionally healthy mother who is comfortable in her feelings of love toward her child does not show these extreme reactions; nor does she show the exaggerated fears and overprotectiveness displayed by the disturbed mother. For the healthy mother the situation with her child is handled without extreme emotional outbursts—she has no need to prove to herself, her son or the world that she loves—she knows she does; nor does she have any feelings of guilt that she must assuage.

A final reason for the disturbed mother's overprotectiveness and exaggerated fears of harm coming to her son is her fear of the sheer destructiveness of her feelings. In fact, many of those people who are so sweet and love everyone and see everything through rose-colored glasses have many of these same feelings. They protest too much; they overreact. In the injury or illness of her son, the mother would see the realization of her underlying feelings of hate which would thus be brought close to the surface and closer to painful recognition. She must do her utmost to prevent all injury and all illness. These fears and overprotective attitudes are necessary to her to keep these hostile feelings fairly well submerged, and thus keep her destructive feelings from becoming unleashed and overwhelming her and her son. The mere thought of such underlying forces produces panic in her.

Mary is 10 years old and has rheumatic heart disease. Unfortunately, her illness has permanently damaged her heart to an extent sufficient to prevent her from leading the sort of life that other children do. Since her most recent attack of acute rheumatic fever, her physician has strongly and repeatedly advised Mary's parents to make her rest in bed at least 2 hours each morning and 2 hours each afternoon. He has also forbidden Mary to run and play and climb with the neighborhood children, although she feels good and states that she can do these activities without getting tired and out of breath. Her already damaged heart would be further weakened (and her life expectancy shortened) by any more episodes of acute rheumatic fever. Therefore, her physician has asked the mother to give Mary an antibiotic medicine by mouth daily to prevent any further attacks of her illness. In spite of repeated and strong admonitions from the physician and in spite of the fact

that Mary's parents should know better, these specific instruc-
tions are not obeyed. The mother always gives in to Mary's
tearful entreaties to go out and play with her friends. Although
the mother excuses this serious violation with the remarks, "I'm
just too soft-hearted," and, "I want her to grow up as normally
as possible," there are other violations. Mary does not always
get her daytime bed rest as she should. She cannot rest until
she has made her bed and finished drying the dishes. The
mother frequently goes out to play bridge. "Now you be sure
you go to bed this afternoon, you hear? I don't want to catch
you playing outside when I get back. Let your friends come
to see you. If I'm not home in time for supper, you'll find some
leftovers in the refrigerator. And don't forget your vitamins."

Mary's mother and father do a lot of entertaining for business
reasons, and the father always brings the guests up to Mary's
room to meet his "sweet little daughter" (and incidentally,
interrupt her sleep and rest at any hour of the night). The
father remarks to his wife, "Mary is so sweet that these people
cannot help but love and feel sorry for her. I hope some of
this rubs off on the boss when he makes out the bonus lists."
Mary never can remember to take her antibiotic pills. As the
mother speaks to the physician who knows how poorly his
advice is being followed, she is very upset, "I cannot do a thing
with Mary. She won't listen . . . forgets her pills, won't rest
. . . wants to play all the time. I'm at my wits' end. Please
speak to her, Doctor, and tell her how important it is to her
life for her to do what she is told."

Here is a situation where the child has a serious disability
in which inadequate care will shorten her life. Although the
importance of such care has been emphasized by the physician,
such care is not being given. The situations described in the
above example are sufficiently obvious to require little additional comment: no antibiotic pills, no rest, no vitamins and
no undisturbed sleep. The father interrupts his daughter's
sleep as a means of advancing his own career. The mother
blames Mary for not doing that which she, the mother, is
responsible for seeing done. The mother tries to pass on to the
doctor her little remaining responsibility, "Please speak to her,
Doctor. . . ." The simple statement, "I cannot do a thing with

Mary," is one that is frequently heard in offices of any physician who sees children. At this point, it should be apparent to the reader that this is as much a problem of the mother as it is a problem of the child. What is there in a mother's feelings toward her child that causes this difficulty in discipline? The specific answer to this question varies with the specific case.

Although the same galaxy of disturbed parent-child emotional relationships exist, there is one difference between the child who was born with his handicap and the child who developed his handicap later in life. In the latter case, the parents and the child can remember better times, especially if the handicap appeared late enough in life so that the child has a permanent and fixed memory of former circumstances. An emotionally healthy parent and child will find the rehabilitation much smoother and easier, and the emotional storms engendered by the disability will subside more quickly and completely than in the previously emotionally disturbed parent and child.

CHAPTER 19

Emotional Aspects of Feeble-mindedness

In the specialist's office or large medical center to which come many children referred by other physicians for consultation on diagnosis and treatment, a large proportion of the problems are those of feeble-mindedness. There are many causes for feeble-mindedness; some cases respond well to treatment; many do not. But in modern society, much can be done for those children who cannot be treated. Despite all the commendable advances in this field of medicine, feeble-mindedness is too often still regarded as a hush-hush problem and a stigma of shame to the family. This unfortunate attitude of shame and the fears that their worst suspicions will be confirmed often cause these parents to delay seeking medical advice. These same attitudes cause parents to deny the diagnosis after it has been made. In the face of such a stark tragedy, for underlying emotional reasons of their own, such parents may also refuse institutionalization for the child when indicated. Fortunately, in recent years there has been a trend away from this ostrichlike attitude and greater interest in studying what can be done to prevent and treat this unfortunate condition.

The question of institutionalization of the feeble-minded child is one of the touchiest and most difficult problems that the parent and the physician must face. At heart this is a highly personal question that can be finally answered only by the parents themselves. Certain general facts must be considered in arriving at a sensible decision. If there are other children in the family, the parents should remember that these healthy children, who will become useful members of society, have many emotional needs which must be satisfied. They cannot and should not be left to shift for themselves while the parents expend all their time, feelings and fortune on the feeble-minded child. Furthermore, it is highly upsetting to the emotional development of the healthy children in the family to live with a feeble-minded brother or sister. They must learn to expect the taunts of other children, the side glances of adult neighbors and even the open remarks of total strangers. As they grow older, they may be ashamed to bring their friends home. They must always offer furtive apologies and excuses. The family finances become depleted following a will-of-the-wisp: dental care to improve appearance; dancing and piano lessons that cannot be appreciated; private tutors; nurses and maids; repeated medical consultations with specialist after specialist; and occasional expensive flirtations with the wild promises of quacks. The family's ability to give the normal children the care and cultural and educational opportunities that they deserve is impaired.

As often happens, the parents might comment, "My other children all love poor little Jimmy. They would hate to have him leave. Why, when the kids make fun of Jimmy, his brothers and sisters always put up a fight." As much as the question might disturb these parents, it should be asked whether their other children are fighting only for their mentally deficient brother or whether they are defending their own wounded pride against a cruel society. In their feelings, the stigma of shame that society puts on their brother rubs off on them. A child has a right to grow up in as peaceful and wholesome an atmosphere as possible. It is very unfair to expose the healthy child to such repeated emotional trauma merely to satisfy the parents' own understandably wounded pride.

The parents who vehemently resist institutionalization and overprotest their love for the child and the child's need for them and sacrifice their lives for their child again protest too much. They overreact. For reasons already discussed (see pp. 14 and 182 (these overreactions may signify only the parents' own mixed feelings toward their disabled child.

Mental defectiveness varies in degree from the minimally defective child who will eventually (granting no great superimposed emotional disturbances) make a fair adjustment in society to the extremely defective child who will need constant care and protection for the rest of his life. The former will be able to support himself in society in tasks commensurate with his abilities; the latter will always need complete support by society. Someone with a mild intellectual impairment and a relatively healthy emotional background may well make a better adjustment in society than someone with a superior intellect and a completely disturbed emotional background.

The feeble-minded child has, it is true, regardless of the degree of his impairment, emotional needs which must be satisfied. Given adequate institutional care, often their needs can be satisfied better in an institution than at home. All too often the feeble-minded child who is kept home, is made the scapegoat for his parent's own emotional problems. It is hypocrisy. It is often the parents' needs and not the child's that are being satisfied.

The physician knows that the different parts of the body develop during the first 3 months that the mother carries her child. After this period of time, development is almost complete, and the baby continues only to increase in size during the rest of the pregnancy. It is also felt that certain factors which affect the mother during the first 3 months of pregnancy may seriously affect the developing baby and, in this way, cause incomplete or faulty development of various parts of the baby's body. One such defect has been shown to be a form of mental deficiency, and one well popularized disease of the mother which has been shown capable of causing this and other defects in the child is German measles. Therefore, prevention or modification of disease in the mother during the first 3 months of pregnancy may aid in preventing many of the defects with which children are born. However, in the majority of cases of feeble-mindedness (as in many cases of children born with other defects), modern medical science cannot find such a relationship to maternal illness or, for that matter, to any cause whatever.

In many instances, feeble-mindedness is the only defect, and there are no other associated defects in the body. In other instances, the feeble-mindedness is associated with other changes inside and outside the body of the child. Some of the illnesses of this latter type are: mongolian idiocy; incomplete formation of the brain; many types of malformation of the brain; hydrocephalalus ("water on the brain"; "large head"); microcephaly ("pinhead"); gargoylism; and brain cysts.

There are other kinds of mental deficiency that, when recognized early by the physician, respond well to treatment. A good and fairly common example of this form is cretinism, a disease in which a child is born with inability to form sufficient amounts of thyroid hormone. If this disease is left untreated sufficiently long, permanent mental deficiency results.

Many forms of mental deficiency are hereditary. It is very important that such forms of deficiency be identified and their hereditary nature explained to the parents. The physician can also trace the origins of the defect in a large number of mentally defective children to diseases contracted early in life. This varied group includes: birth injury to the brain; meningitis; encephalitis ("brain fever"); brain and head injuries occurring later in life; kernicterus (a disease resulting from Rh blood reactions between mother and child); and repeated severe insulin reactions in the diabetic child.

Although there are many cases of feeble-mindedness in which the cause can be found and sometimes removed with significant consequent improvement in mental function, there are many more cases in which the cause is not known. However, in recent years, with increased study of feeble-minded children and their backgrounds, it has become startlingly apparent that at least some such cases are due to emotional causes.

Part of this group had previously suffered some damage to the brain from injury or disease. Their defects included various disturbances in walking, talking, writing, balance, co-ordination, sight, hearing, touch and bowel and bladder control. With these gross handicaps, resulting from definite brain injury, untrained observers may make the unwarranted generalization that the child is also feeble-minded. This is a red herring. Careful study of these children and their parents reveal much evidence of severe emotional disturbance. Collaborative studies by physicians reveal that long before such children are injured, his parents have the same highly disturbed underlying emotions seen in the parents of the physically handicapped child already discussed. With the tacit understanding and outright sympathy of a highly misinformed and superstitious society, it is all too easy for the emotionally disturbed parent to find in his apparently "brain damaged" child, the convenient escape hatch for his own overwhelming and disturbing emotions. By using his child as the object through whom is revealed the parent's own submerged destructive feelings, the parent can find surcease from the flames of his own warped passions. The parent, by finding such release for the tension within himself, saves himself, but does so at the price of his child's mental integrity. These destructive feelings and the mechanism for their release from the parent are completely hidden beneath the surface and are revealed only by the most painstakingly careful examination of the emotional life of child and parent. Despite the fact that these hostile feelings are so subtly and completely hidden beneath the facade that the parent presents to society and to himself, their destructive effects are far-reaching and tragic—feeble-mindedness. The causes are hidden; the effect, obvious.

For example, the apparent calm of an unhealthy parent-child relationship may suddenly and violently be disrupted by disease or injury to the child's brain. The seeds of hate, never quite asleep, lie within the sick parent, forever threatening to erupt and destroy the parent or someone near to him. The child cannot escape this inoculation of hate. It may affect him sufficiently to make him unable to function effectively in society (feeble-mindedness and schizophrenia), or the child may be inoculated and affected as his parents were before him, and thus be unable to have a healthy relationship with those close to him (for example, sexual deviations, various phobias and delinquency). One or the other possibility must occur unless medical help is sought. Which alternative will actually occur depends on the life-situations which exist.

Therefore, when such a parent is confronted with the unexpected and overwhelming event of a disease or an injury to the child's brain, the underlying emotions of hate are touched off. The event is too close to the destructive feelings, however deep and inapparent such feelings may be to the parent and to those about him. In the emergency of the injury, the accompanying guilt, as already described with the handicapped child, swells and rises closer to the surface. The parent will blame himself mercilessly in a vain attempt to assuage his guilt. He totally resists well-meaning efforts at consolation. At this point, the physician may mention feeble-mindedness as a possible complication. Or, the disease or injury may not even be of a type to cause the physician to consider this complication. However, a chance remark by a nurse, a hospital orderly or a relative may be overheard by the parent. Thus, for the first time since the child's birth, the parent will find an acceptable outlet for his own forbidden and destructive feelings. The parent, whose own pent-up emotions have been straining for release, has found suddenly and fortuitously the means of showing his hate toward his child in a manner that both the parent and society will accept. "The poor boy is a hopeless idiot; the brain injury made him that way." As the parent's hate finds a suitable object, the brain-injured child, to act upon, the parent's former panic is partially relieved. Now the confused and thoroughly frightened child can also find relief from his own pent-up tensions and fear of his parent's destructiveness by a retreat to earlier modes of behavior (see p. 68). By doing so, by showing infantile forms of behavior at an age when such behavior should be long past, he gives the superficial appearance of feeble-mindedness. This young child will wallow helplessly in a permanent stage of babyhood. Depending on previous life experiences, either he will have intemperate outbursts of biting, screaming, kicking and soiling, or he will be in a complacent stage of accepting everything in a dull, listless vegetative existence. This destructive parent-child adjustment will have to hold to prevent the recurrence of the previous panic of parent and child. Unless detected and interrupted, this succession of events will continue unalterably until the death of the child. The only hope

—and the really final proof—for this tragic parent-child relationship is the marked improvement and response of the
afflicted child to appropriate medical treatment for both child
and parent.

What if the child resists being the scapegoat in this manner?
What if the child never had been hurt or ill in this manner, and
the parent never had chanced upon this possible solution to
his difficulties? Depending on life experiences specific to the
parent and undoubtedly on many other poorly understood
factors, the parent must find an outlet for his tensions after
they build up beyond a certain critical level. In such situations
where the parent cannot find the outlet through his child
(feeble-mindedness, delinquency, childhood sexual problems
and other problems already discussed), it is not unusual to
see these unrequited factors operating to a greater or lesser
degree in certain diseases in the parent. Examples of such
diseases are acute depression, alcoholism, anxiety states, hyper-
thyroidism, peptic ulcer, chronic ulcerative colitis, nervous
heart, hypertension, migraine and neurodermatitis ("nervous
eczema"). Or, when the parent cannot find an outlet through
either his child or within himself, he will release these tensions
in disturbed relationships with his fellow human beings:
divorce action, inability to hold a job and to establish and
maintain real friendships.

There are some cases of feeble-mindedness, present from
birth, which also serve as an outlet for the parents' disturbed
emotions. The same parental problems and needs are present,
but in such cases, the parent found the necessary outlet much
earlier in the child's life, often even conjured up in the parents'
fears before the child's birth or at birth. "When I was carrying
Billy, he was so active that I was afraid he would be like my
husband's mentally defective sister who runs wild all over
the house, beats her head against the wall and smashes things."

At this point, an example of an actual case of "feeble-
mindedness" produced by the sick emotions of the parent will
help to clarify some of the above statements. Many of the
principles learned by collaborative therapy from this case have

been shown to apply, in varying degrees, to many cases of feeble-mindedness, regardless of the cause.

Dickie is a handsome, brown-haired, husky, 5-year-old who was brought to the physician by his mother because of "mental retardation." While in the waiting room, he sat quietly in his chair and seemed to be completely oblivious of his surroundings. He showed no response to the other children, the ringing telephones, the nurse's greeting or even to his mother when she called him. His mother had to go to him and lead him like a baby. Complete studies revealed no known physical cause for the apparent deficiency. The examination revealed no physical abnormalities. All the studies on the spinal fluid, the blood and the urine were normal. Special and complete examinations of the nervous system including the reflexes were all normal. X-ray pictures of the head, a brainwave and special hearing tests were similarly normal. The only abnormality found during this extensive study was the I.Q., which showed the child to be grossly deficient. However, the physician found from his questioning that Dickie had reached for and grasped objects, sat up alone, walked with and then without support, held a spoon, learned bowel and bladder control, and begun to talk, all at the normally expected ages. In fact, Dickie had developed completely normally until he was 3 years old when his sister was born. Since that time, the boy apparently had lost his vocabulary and said only one thing over and over again all day long. "Make Dickie a good boy. Make Dickie a good boy." Since 3 years of age, Dickie had showed marked abnormalities in behavior whereas prior to this time his behavior had been similar to that of other children his own age. Aside from occasionally pushing and kicking his little 2-year-old sister, Dickie had no contact with the world around him. He did not play with other children; he showed no interest in participating in the usual family activities. When eating, he noisily gorged himself with food "like an animal." He would pick up the food with his hands, stuff his mouth and bolt the food down. He soiled himself on occasion and had lost his previous bladder control both for daytime and nighttime. Dickie's mother was amused, because he would sit down to urinate, although formerly he used to stand. Dickie constantly interrupted the examination by shrill cries and screams. He made no effort to wipe away the saliva which drooled from his mouth. Dickie whirled and darted about the room without any apparent purpose. He hopped about and flapped his arms like a bird.

[Dickie's behavior was much different from that of a healthy 5-year-old. He had progressed normally with his learning until 3 years of age. After that, there was not only lack of progress but also actual loss of that which had already been learned. Was he actually mentally deficient? Why the sudden deterioration at 3 years of age? It should be noted that there was no injury or illness at that time—only the birth of his sister.]

As part of his complete study of the emotional backgrounds of Dickie and his parents, the physician questioned the mother about her past life. The physician took 2 whole hours that day with the mother, asking her questions and listening to her. He could not get any coherent story. He never received a direct answer to a question. It was almost impossible to communicate with her. An avalanche of words, a kaleidoscope of disjointed thoughts engulfed him. Despite this verbiage, some of which referred to tragic events in her past life, Dickie's mother maintained the same wooden smile. The chain-smoking clouded the apparent calm of her feelings. The physician recognized that this flow of words suggested a severe disturbance in the mother. However, it was only after seeing the mother a number of times that he could begin to discern a pattern to her disturbance.

The smile never faded; the smoking never ceased. As the mother interrupted her usual apparently meaningless chatter with a description of an extremely tragic event in her past life, no noticeable emotion appeared in either her voice or feelings.

Dickie's mother, Mrs. B., described how her own father abandoned her mother and brother a few months before her own birth. The father refused to contribute to the support of the family until legal action was taken by welfare agencies. Immediately after she completed her description of this tragedy, she said, with the same fixed smile, "I always loved Daddy." In fact, this phrase, as the interview progressed, became her motto and accompanied every reference to her father.

All these references revealed his glaring and complete lack of any affection for his family. But, "I always loved Daddy." During her childhood, Mrs. B. never saw her father, but she received Christmas cards, and a quarter was always enclosed as a Christmas present. The Christmas card and the quarter were repeated annually until she was married. This was the full extent of the father's yearly gifts to his daughter who said she loved him. He did not attend her wedding or send her any wedding gift. In spite of the court order, the father never gave one cent to his wife for the support of his family. His wife, Dickie's maternal grandmother, did nothing to insist that the court order for the support of herself and her children be enforced. Through the years, the father never wrote to his wife. However, on rare occasions he did write a long letter to his own mother who lived only a short subway ride away. When Dickie's mother was a young girl, she often visited this grandmother and avidly read the long letters that her father wrote to his own mother but which his wife and daughter never received. She thirsted for any information about her father. "I always loved Daddy." Her own mother never said anything. Through these letters, Mrs. B. learned and later confirmed the fact that her father had become a millionaire whose yearly income was fabulous. He traveled around Europe as a business tycoon and lavished great sums of money on "wine, women and song." Although he sent nothing, except for the Christmas quarter to either his own wife or daughter, it was his custom to enclose $3.00 with his annual Easter card to his mother. When the brother was in high school, the father began sending him $25 a week for his personal use. The father always sent this money through the boy's paternal grandmother. The father also offered to pay for his son's education if he wished to go to business school. Nothing was offered to the daughter (Mrs. B.) or his wife.

[The facts speak for themselves. Despite Mrs. B.'s wooden smile and repeated protestations of love for her father, one must wonder. She protests too much. The father's behavior was too bizarre to elicit any reaction but hate.]

After the marriage of Dickie's mother, her father occasionally visited her and her new family. He would pop in completely unannounced, remain for a few days to a few weeks and, without a word, leave. Dickie's mother never knew when he was coming or going. During these visits he never contributed any money whatever to his daughter and her struggling family. He never even suggested that his daughter or any member of her family accompany him to the opera, the symphony or the Broadway hit shows. His main topic of conversation with the family consisted of business discussions and detailed analyses of past and current financial trends. He would spend most of his time in the house, absorbed alone in reading the financial journals and the stock market quotations. He rarely paid any attention to his daughter, her husband or her children. He never asked how his daughter or her family were doing. In the face of their poverty, his only other conversational topic consisted almost entirely of his travels, what he had seen and what he had done. He delighted in describing how well he held his own with the "great brains" of the world. In a continuous monologue, he repeated verbatim his conversations with intellectuals he knew, discussing all the fine shades of economic and philosophic thought. He was truly a man of the world to whom no doors of academic and intellectual pursuits were closed. But the family to whom he described all this were plain people without the background to understand. They listened respectfully without interrupting. The father droned on and on. There was no common meeting ground. The family accepted the situation and saw nothing unusual in it. The father never showed the slightest interest in Dickie's problem.

[The father's previous cold and self-centered attitude continued. The daughter continued to "love Daddy." From what has already been discussed in this book, the reader will undoubtedly wonder what type of woman would accept the situation imposed on her by a man of this type. Only after many difficult hours of painstaking sifting of words and feelings that held together like sand did the physician obtain from Mrs. B. a clearer picture of Dickie's maternal grandmother. It will be recalled that a welfare agency and not the grandmother had instituted legal action to obtain financial support from the father who had abandoned his family. Also, it will be recalled that despite her needs and the support of the court action, the maternal grandmother chose to struggle as best she could on her own and did nothing to insist that the court order be enforced. By her failure to take a firm stand in this matter, the maternal grandmother was only giving permission and actually fostering her husband's means of showing his hostility to his family. The differences between husband and wife that accounted for the separation can only be conjectured. As the physician assembled the shredded pieces of Mrs. B.'s life story he repeatedly saw the parallelism of the underlying hostility between Mrs. B.'s father and mother and between Mrs. B. and her father. He also began to perceive similar feelings between Dickie and his mother.]

Dickie's grandmother was strict and suspicious. Deserted by her husband during her pregnancy, refused support by him when he was well able to give it, Dickie's maternal grandmother chose to accept in silence the role of the wronged woman. She did not struggle. She dedicated herself completely to her family and devoted all her energies to a little dress shop. However, evidences of her poorly contained rage gushed out on her daughter, Dickie's mother. With the same wooden smile with which she described her father, Mrs. B. stated that her own mother "beat me every day of my life. My [older] brother was the favorite and always got off scot-free." Sam, her brother, was 4 years older than Dickie's mother. He had gone to college, knew 3 languages and learned to hold his own in discussions with his father. In her conversation with the physician, with its myriad, varied unconnected thoughts, she tended to belittle the intellectual achievements of her husband and herself in comparison with the magnificent intellectual achievements of her father and brother. "My husband and I were lucky to get through high school; my Daddy and brother have many college degrees."

The daily beatings from her mother until her 'teens were administered without reason and often with the pious admonition, "This will make you a good girl." As a girl, Mrs. B. had to work each afternoon and evening, week-ends included, in her mother's dress shop while her brother came and went as he chose (as his father did). Dickie's mother consistently shied away from any discussion of her mother and her own feelings toward her. However, Dickie's mother did mention one bizarre incident. She vividly described, with the same fixed smile her mother's reaction when she, Dickie's mother, narrowly escaped death. While dining in a restaurant on a teen-age date, there was a sudden explosion in the kitchen, and within minutes, flames and terror spread through the restaurant. Mrs. B. and her date escaped with only minor cuts. When she arrived home, terrified, exhausted and disheveled, her mother, instead of trying to find out what had happened and comforting her terrified daughter, immediately flew into an uncontrollable rage and started screaming and violently slapping her daughter's face with her open hand. "What have you done? What have you done?"

[It is apparent that Dickie's mother had grave emotional problems with her own mother as with her father. Mrs. B. could not give any more information about her own mother in spite of many, many hours of interview with her physician. After what has already been said and shown previously, it would be naive to assume that the maternal grandmother's hostility and rage all resulted from, and solely from, her unhappy marriage. Blaming emotional disturbances on "marital incompatibility," "mental cruelty," divorce and separation is like placing the cart before the horse. An overwhelming number of cases of marital incompatibility and related legal solutions stem from pre-existing emotional problems in both partners. It is these pre-existing problems of the parents that adversely affect the child's developing conscience and emotional make-up. These legal solutions do nothing to change the fundamental emotional maladjustments of the parents. These maladjustments may become less obvious as the superficial environmental factors which brought them to the surface are removed by the divorce or the separation. But, although submerged, the causes of these maladjustments remain to affect both parents and growing children. Dickie's mother was presumably so terrified by her hostile feelings toward her own mother and father that she was unable to discuss her feelings toward them at all.

[It was clear that Dickie's mother also had hostile feelings toward her brother. She could not hide her rare outbursts of resentment at the different manner in which her parents treated her and her brother. Such seething hate had to find an outlet. This outlet was provided when Dickie's young sister was born. Here was a situation which closely resembled the earlier situation between Mrs. B. and her own older brother. The memories of old injustices and present resentments against her brother still rankled Mrs. B. Dickie, who in the new family situation held a position similar to that of his uncle in the old family situation, became the object against which she directed all her pent-up hatreds. Here is another clear example of why one particular child becomes the scapegoat for a parent's emotional disturbances while another child escapes relatively unscathed (see p. 127).

[An additional ironic twist to this tragic situation is that Dickie apparently lacked that quality most admired by this family: a superior intellect. Or would not this apparent feeble-mindedness of the grandson and nephew be the sweetest possible revenge against a father and brother who revered above all else a superior intellect?]

In later sessions with the physician the relationship between this background information and the mother's problem with Dickie became slowly apparent. The mother behaved in a very bizarre and hostile way toward her son. One day while waiting for the physician in his office, Dickie vomited all over himself. The mother looked up completely unperturbed and returned to her magazine. On another occasion, Dickie spilled over his head the bottle of red paint by the children's drawing board. The mother shrugged her shoulders and, without any change in facial expression, wordlessly brought Dickie to the sink and turned on the faucet so the water poured over his head.

When the mother was being interviewed separately by the physician, she described Dickie's up-bringing. Every day from 10:00 A.M. until 11:30 A.M. she would strap 5-year-old Dickie to a high chair and then, on a blackboard placed in front of him, slowly trace out the letters of the alphabet while repeating them verbally. She felt certain that all this time spent with the child in this way would cure him of his feeble-mindedness and make him as smart as his (maternal) grandfather and uncle. Every day from 1:00 P.M. until 2:00 P.M., the alarm clock would ring and Dickie's mother would say, "Go make wee-wee." She was very proud of Dickie's ability to urinate when told to do so. She laughingly added that her son always sat down to urinate. Mrs. B. had another strange habit; she kept all the cereal boxes half full "so he wouldn't have an accident and mess everything up. I should follow him around the house more than I do. The way he runs around the house and jumps on the bed worries me. He's already ruined two mattresses. And our wedding dishes—they're practically all smashed. I'm afraid he'll get badly hurt some day."

[There is no warmth toward her son, only an insistence on strict adherence to a schedule which the mother imagines is the proper thing to do. Her attempt to make her son smart like the father and brother that she holds in awe is similarly rigid, cold and bizarre. It should be noted that one of the few times that the mother showed any spark of feeling was when she described how her son urinated like a woman. Her exaggerated precautions against an accident and her complete failure to set limits to her son's destructive actions around the house are more indications of her submerged rage (see p. 182) and her permissiveness. She cannot say, "No"! The hate and the deprivation to which she had been exposed as a child determined her relationship to her son. Having never gained love, she is unable to give any. The problems of one generation have been passed on to the next.]

Dickie's father, as one would expect from the fact that he did marry and remained presumably comfortably married to such a woman, also had bizarre reactions. He was a nonentity who spent all his time at home in the garage tinkering with his car. He religiously overhauled the motor of his car, taking it apart and putting it together again, every week-end. Since the motor was taken apart over week-ends, the car never could be used for family week-end jaunts.

Faced with the cold hatred of his mother and receiving neither warmth nor emotional support from his father, Dickie had been terrified. He had sought escape from this terror by retreating to earlier modes of behavior, by acting much younger than his age (see p. 68). He tried to retreat to a previous mode of behavior during which life had been more comfortable. By behaving as though he were much younger than his true age, Dickie appeared to be mentally retarded.

The mother was seen 3 times a week for 1 hour at a time over a period of many months while the son was seen by another physician at the same time. Weekly the two physicians would confer and exchange information concerning all the data and feelings obtained by each physician in the preceding interviews. This scattered fragmentary information was slowly pieced together to reveal the interrelationships between mother and son. As new and specific feelings of either mother or son came to the surface and revealed themselves, the effect of such feelings upon the other person was noted. The feelings and the reactions of one always dovetailed with the feelings and the reactions of the other. As the hours progressed and the physicians began to know their patients better, the physicians could often predict with amazing accuracy how one would react to the feelings and the behavior of the other. By talking to the physician, the deep feelings were slowly and painfully brought to the surface of hazy awareness. The mother slowly began to realize that she had some problems—serious problems —that had a direct bearing on her son's illness. She then wanted medical help. During this long and difficult period of gentle uncovering of her underlying rage and hate from the deprivation of love, the mother began slowly to show some emotion. Although her wooden smile persisted, her eyes would fill with tears when she mentioned either her mother or her father.

In the meantime, as the mother for the first time in her life found herself able to relate her true feelings to someone without fear of punishment, her underlying need to let some of her pent-up hatred out through her son slowly receded. While Dickie was being seen by the other physician and the mother's hatred toward her son slowly ebbed away, a change in Dickie's behavior slowly became discernible. The physician was warm and kind to Dickie; he brought his little patient candy, potato chips and soda pop before each interview. More important, he showed his warmth and kindness by his feelings toward Dickie. Dickie was slowly and painfully learning that people could have feelings other than hate toward him and that he could live comfortably in the present with no longer any need to retreat to early stages of behavior. The physician played games with Dickie. When, during play, Dickie was faced with an event that caused rage (as when the blocks fell down), the physician restrained him from throwing a block through the closed window. The physician told him that he understood how angry Dickie could be but that certain things just are not done. The physician set definite limits to the destructiveness of Dickie's rage, something his mother, in her guilt, had been unable to do. The physician also showed Dickie by example that rage was acceptable as long as it was not destructive. It was now becoming safe for Dickie to return to a mode of behavior consistent with that of his age. He began to speak again, looked forward to seeing his doctor (with whom he had established a close and comfortable relationship), and began to act his age.

In short, the proof of the pudding was Dickie's slow but definite return from apparent feeble-mindedness to emotional and intellectual health.

[This mother's seething hate almost found a revenge possibly greater than death itself. Death happens and is finished. Feeble-mindedness goes on and on.]

CHAPTER 20

Death of the Parent and a Digression on Divorce

To the growing child the birth of a brother or a sister is no less a mystery than the death of a parent. The birth of a brother or a sister is easier for the child to understand. The child can see, hear and feel the new infant. Although he may envy and resent the new arrival, he has, mixed with these feelings, curiosity and pride. Like a new household possession, the baby gives ever-present tangible reminders of its presence. However, death is a much more difficult concept for the young child to understand. What is death? "Daddy, where is Mommy?" "Daddy, when is Mommy coming back?" "Why did Mommy leave?" "Doesn't Mommy love me any more?" "Did she leave me because I was naughty?"

At the time of a death, the adults are all wrapped up in their own feelings. Some cry inconsolably. Some sit in a stony silence. Others reminisce endlessly. The death becomes the rare occasion for a family reunion. While the necessary funeral arrangements are made, the children are frequently left to shift for themselves or are sent away to be cared for by relatives or neighbors during this period of upheaval. As much as possible is done to shield the child from the shock of death. Often it is felt that the child is too young to understand fully all the implications of the tragedy that has just occurred. When the child does show any feelings, the adults display a naive confidence in the child's emotional resiliency, his ability to bounce back. "She'll get over it. All children do." When the adults do think of the child's loss, they frequently think of the child's immediate loss. "Who will feed her?" "Who will buy her clothes and dress her?" "Now the mother must go to work and earn money for her." "She'll be all alone." "Will the company's pension plan be enough?" "Did he have enough insurance?" "How can they take care of the mortgage?" "What can the relatives contribute to tide the family over the present?"

With the shock of their bereavement still fresh, relatives and friends make well-meaning and sympathetic promises of help to the family, promises that may never be kept. There is much understandable concern for the surviving parent. "The poor mother (or the poor father)! What will she do now with all these children? She's all alone!" Again the thought recurs that the child will get over his loss, will bounce back. The hard truth is that the surviving parent probably will return to emotional equilibrium and will adjust to the new situation while the child might carry scars throughout life.

The child is extremely dependent upon the parent for his needs. The specific needs and the extent of this dependency vary as the child grows older. As an infant, he is totally dependent upon his parents. He is helpless. He must be fed, clothed, loved, taught, moved about and protected from the dangers in his surroundings. Without such parental protection, he will die. In short, he must be cared for emotionally and materially. As the child gets older, new needs will develop, and old needs will change. The child's need to know that there is someone near on whom he can depend continues, and this need persists through adult life. The most important need is that of love. It is either there or not. The child must know by the mutual exchange of feelings between himself and the parent that he is loved. Empty tokens of love, unaccompanied by feelings of love, do not satisfy this fundamental need of life. The lollypop or the new bicycle, used as a sop, totally unaccompanied by feelings of love, do not satisfy this need. As the child grows up, he becomes able to provide some of his own material needs. However, his emotional needs continue. Many previous examples have shown that the way in which these emotional needs are gratified does much to determine emotional health and disease.

Lest this discussion sound too arbitrary, it should be emphasized that the emotional and material needs are not separate entities to be considered entirely apart from each other. Rather, they are inextricably blended together. This blending is readily apparent in the helpless child for whom the provision of food, shelter and clothing necessary to life are tangible tokens of being cared for and of being loved. This blending of emotional and material needs is less apparent in the older child and adult. The lollypop is hardly necessary for life, but it serves as a wonderful reminder and tangible token of the fact that the child's parents care for him. In later life the box of candy or the dozen roses serve the same purpose. However, for both child and adult, the accompanying feelings determine whether the lollypop, the box of candy, or the roses are symbols of love or act as bribes, means of assuaging guilt or forestalling antici- pated expressions of rage.

Many examples in this book have shown the dire effects of inoculating the child with sick emotions, maliciously disguised and presented as love while at the same time fully providing for food, clothing and shelter. An extreme example is provided by infants in some foundling homes who show a disturbingly higher rate of death and emotional and physical diseases than infants in other foundling homes. In both types of foundling homes, the same standards of food, clothing, shelter and pre- vention of infection prevail. However, in the home with the alarming disease and death rate, there is less exchange of feel- ings between the helpless lonely babies and the nurses and the matrons who rush from baby to baby, holding them only long enough to complete the necessary routine care. It is all in a day's work. Even when they do stop to go through the motions of cuddling and cooing over the child, it is all done as a part of the necessary routine. There is little feeling; their thoughts frequently lie elsewhere. The children's need for love remains ungratified. Many die or become ill.

By unwitting and subtle communications and by purposeful teaching and imitation, the child learns and acquires the super- ficial and deep emotional values and quirks of his parents. The child becomes strongly attached by example and memory to the parent who gratifies his needs and whose own feelings and actions the child imitates. The child is born with both the need and the potential for emotion. He is not born with any specific emotion. He is not born with love or hate or any of their many variations. These specific emotions and the values attached to them are learned completely from those upon whom he depends and whom he imitates. Therefore, the parent is the most important part of the child's environment.

The child (and the adult) needs to know that there is someone near on whom he can depend for the gratification of his needs. When death removes the one who provides these needs, an immediate vacuum and tension is created in the child. The props have been removed. All the feelings and memories which united child to parent have been severed. Unable to grasp the concept of time, the young child cannot comprehend the meaning of death, why death and what follows death. Why and where has the departed parent gone? All that the child can understand is that the one who loved him and gratified his needs has departed. He feels that the loved one has abandoned him. He is confused and angry at being left alone. But he must keep these feelings to himself. He cannot show anger. No one can show anger in the presence of death. Only sorrow is permitted. "Speak kindly of the dead." Unable to pour his feelings out on the world about him, these feelings become bottled up within him. In this way, these feelings of anger become that part of the individual's emotional life which lies submerged beneath the surface. But being submerged beneath the surface does not mean, as already noted, that it lies passively dormant. It continues to affect the attitudes and the reactions of the individual to the people and the events about him. Unless the vacuum created by the death of the parent is filled (see the next chapter on adoption) and unless the tensions created by the death are relieved, the process of imitation of the departed parent will be unfinished and possibly blighted, and anger will persist.

These submerged feelings of anger are present in any young child who loves and loses a parent. The surviving parent or responsible relatives or guardians should recognize the fact that the child has many mixed feelings at such a time. With genuine feeling and sympathy, the responsible adult should permit the child to express his feelings and ask his questions. The adult should recognize that here is another human being, albeit small and inarticulate, who also has feelings and questions. His feelings may not take on the adult pattern of grief and loss, but they are nevertheless real and must be recognized. In paying understandable heed to the grief-stricken adults, it is unfair to the child to neglect his feelings. "He is too small to know." "Let us shield him from all this." Although the confusion and the quiet manner of the child at the time of death may belie the underlying turmoil, his true feelings seep out later in questions, play and dreams. He will frequently ask, "Where has Daddy gone?" "Where is heaven?" "Why did Daddy leave me?" "Doesn't Daddy love me?" "Did I do something wrong?" The little boy or girl will play hospital or doctor or nurse to re-enact the disturbing events. In his play, toy automobiles will crash, dolls will be injured, operations will take place, and buildings and piles of blocks will tumble. Airplanes and special rocket ships will soar almost to heaven. Toy child dolls will be naughty, and therefore toy parent dolls will leave them. Games with toy weapons of destruction will either be avoided entirely or will be played again and again, depending on the child's specific feelings toward the death. In dreams, departed parents will return to the child with love and gifts; children will play happily at favorite games; or nightmares of death and destruction will recur.

The emotionally healthy child who can show and talk about all his mixed feelings which are sympathetically understood by the grown-ups around him will have the same reactions. But these reactions are not too severe and will last only a limited time. For the most part, the child's grief will slowly disappear and will be replaced by an acceptance of the new situation. He will remember his father or mother as a truly fine person. He will strive to continue to imitate his idealized concept of that parent. The scars of the former turmoil will remain, but they are not deep and incapacitating.

If the child becomes unduly disturbed or withdrawn following the death of a parent, and if this persists, many factors may be responsible. The relations of the child with the departed parent may have been upsetting. The relations of the child with the surviving parent may be faulty. The actual death and the circumstances and feelings surrounding it may have been, of their very nature, upsetting to the child and poorly handled by the adults. For example, a pain-laden and lingering death or a death preceded by amputation or other obviously mutilating surgery or disease may affect the child adversely. The brutal admonition, "Be quiet, or you'll kill your poor Mommy," is a fearsome memory for the child to recall following the death. The frequent reminder, "Your Mommy died giving birth to you," is similarly a cruel and uncalled for statement. Making the child feel responsible for the death of a parent may brutally undermine the child's ability to develop warm relationships with other people of the same sex as the departed parent. The barbaric custom of having the child kiss the dead parent becomes the seed for many haunting and frightening memories. A death ushered in gradually by a prolonged illness is met differently by the child (and the adults) than a death which comes abruptly and unexpectedly.

With the many feelings which exist between the child and his mother and father during the first romance stage, the feelings accompanying and following a death which occurs at this time will be influenced by the emotions of this stage in addition to the emotions already discussed. If the rivalries of the first romance stage of development already discussed are poorly handled by the parents, the bereaved child will be more disturbed by his parent's death. Should the parent of the same sex die during the height of this stage of the child's development (and during the height of the healthy or exaggerated rivalry of this stage), the feelings of anger and guilt generated by this rivalry and subsequent death will echo through all the child's future in his feelings and actions. His future may be tainted forever. The child has not had a chance to settle the mixed feelings of love and hate which accompany this rivalry. The parent dies before this conflict could be settled as it often is at the end of the first romance stage of development.

"Speak kindly of the dead." Such sentiments are very confusing to that child who knows from past experiences with the departed parent that the latter's feelings and actions could leave few pleasant memories. It is hypocrisy to expect the child to hold reverent memories of someone he actually

detested or who he knew detested him. Under such circumstances it is confusing and unreal for the child to listen to the
surviving parent credit the departed one with virtues which
the child knows the departed one never had. "Your poor
father, Mary, was the most considerate and loving husband
and father anyone could ever have." Actually, however, the
father had been an old roué and was drunk much of the time;
Mary knew it; so did the rest of the family and the children in
the neighborhood. The emotionally healthy child thinks of his
dead parent as a very fine person, even tending to exaggerate
his virtues. He will attempt to imitate these virtues.

If the child is told fancy lies about the departed parent,
and he knows they are lies, he will not imitate this false, though
ideal behavior attributed to the departed parent, nor will he
learn to tell the truth himself. The mother, by refusing to
admit that the departed parent had evil qualities (when the
child remembers otherwise), has never once censured those
evil feelings and actions which the child knows existed. By
refusing to censure the evil of which both mother and child
are aware and by only speaking good of the dead father who
was evil, the mother is creating a loophole. By example, the
child is learning that his mother does not censure evil and this
leads the child to expect that should he similarly do evil, his
mother will cover up for him too. In this way she fosters in
the child the evil that she tries to deny in the dead parent. In
addition, this child must contend with other emotional forces.
If the departed parent had been mean and cruel to the child
during life, the child would have had additional reasons to
harbor many understandable feelings of anger against the
departed parent. The desire to punish the evil parent would
have appeared with the anger. In the death of the parent the
child would see his parent punished, but it is a horrible punishment, complete and final. The child had wished to punish;
the parent is punished; the parent is dead. It is more than the
child could have bargained for. Could his own wishes to
punish the parent have been responsible for this horrible
event? Guilt appears. What would happen if he were to show
anger again in the future toward other people? He becomes
terror-stricken at the thought of ever again showing or even

admitting to feelings of anger. The previous feelings of anger against the departed parent which have had no opportunity to become resolved remain seething within him. The mother, by her denial of the facts, permits the child no way of ridding himself of all this pent-up anger and guilt. He must continue to contain all this turmoil within himself. With the guilt are sown the seeds for future brooding melancholy or other forms of depressed feelings and, sometimes, the complete and final solution to depressed states—self-destruction.

These same feelings of anger and guilt occur in the child whose parent has just committed suicide, and, again, these feelings are intensified if the previous child-parent relationship had been unhealthy. Such a unique event has distinct effects upon the child. Any individual who commits suicide has been in a state of serious emotional turmoil in the period immediately preceding and most often for long periods of time prior to the suicide. While in such a highly disturbed state, the parent could not help but inoculate his child with at least some of those highly destructive feelings which led to the suicide. Another factor to be considered is the child's knowledge that the parent with his own hand and of his own will left him, the child. "Didn't Daddy love me?" "Why did he leave?" "Was I naughty?" The highly impressionable child always will carry the memory of his father's solution to life's problems. The suicide has shown the child an example, in his own family, of inability and refusal to face life's problems. In his future life, when faced with a serious problem, he may see in his parent's example permission similarly to refuse to face his own problems. With such a background, it is not at all uncommon to see alcoholism, desertion and suicide appear. Basically, it is in the previous hostile parent-child relationships and not in heredity that one should look for the causes of suicide.

What should the surviving parent tell the child when a suicide has occurred? The answer to this question often defies an answer and probably is answered best by the feelings of the surviving parent. As in all cases of death of a parent, the reaction of the surviving parent to the death and the feelings of this parent toward the deceased and toward the children will determine how the death will be handled with the children. It is probably better in this tragic situation for the surviving parent to tell the truth to the child without giving any unnecessary details rather than have the child inadvertently learn the truth later in life and have all his dreams shattered. As part of the truth, it should be stated that the departed parent was very sick and that taking his own life was very foolish and wrong. The child should definitely know that there can be no excuse for such an act. As in all instances of death in a parent, but even more true in the case of a parent who has committed suicide, the child should be permitted and encouraged to express himself. When the child asks questions about the departed one, the surviving parent should emphasize only the happy, good and healthy times shared by the child and the departed parent prior to the events that led to the suicide—provided, of course, that happy, good and healthy times were actually shared.

The advice that the surviving parent should tell the truth does not mean that she should constantly bring up on her own accord and repeatedly emphasize all that was wrong (and none that was good) with the departed one. This is as cruel and destructive to the child as the fabrication of false virtues. In either case, the child becomes the whipping boy for the hatred of the surviving parent for the former marital partner. By dwelling at great length, without provocation by the child, on the vices of the departed one, the surviving parent reveals to the child her own intense interest and total preoccupation with these vices. In this way, the surviving parent encourages in the child those vices which she repeatedly deplores in the dead one.

What should the surviving parent say about a departed one who had many vices about which the child knows? When the child asks, tell the simple short truth in response to his specific questions. Details which are not requested need not and should not be given. Long-winded harangues only emphasize to the child the surviving parent's own interest in the vices being discussed or the surviving parent's own marital problems with the deceased. Simply and at no unreasonable length, tell the child that such vices are wrong. Do not tell the child, "Don't let me ever catch you doing that yourself." Such a statement only opens up to the child new vistas for his own future actions. Such a statement tells the child that the surviving parent expects that at some future time the child might also develop the same vices. Why should a parent who is certain of his and his child's own morality fear that the child can or will go wrong?

The surviving parent does not, under any circumstances and for any excuse, tell the child any of the departed parent's vices of which the child is not aware. The surviving parent does not lie to the child about what the child already knows, but the parent does not have to give the child new fuel for thought. The parent does not have to use the child as a whipping boy to gratify his or her own emotional needs and to act as an escape hatch for the parent's own angry feelings toward the departed one. The child himself gives the cue, and the parent who loves and understands the child will recognize the child's needs without the necessity of going verbally into most of this material. The parent and the child with a good underlying healthy exchange of feelings know what the situation is without the need for too much discussion. Under such circumstances usually little of this need be discussed verbally. It is often in the mutual honest exchange of healthy feelings that the above points are made by parent to child.

These same principles apply to the feelings of the child toward the death of a brother or a sister or any close relatives or friends. For instance, if the surviving child had been in a stage of intense competition with the departed brother or sister, albeit the competition had been well disguised, the surviving child has lost a brother or a sister during a period of rivalry. All brothers and sisters go through periods of healthy rivalry with each other, competing for many things but often especially for their parents' affections. However, in this instance, the loss occurred before the mutual feelings of anger could be resolved with time and healthy parent-child relationships and child-child relationships. As in the case of the child who lost the parent of the same sex during the first romance stage, this anger persists unresolved and becomes submerged with other underlying but important feelings. If the competition was quite extreme, the death of one child can have a shattering effect upon the other. In his confused state of thought he feels that his unbridled anger contributed to the death of his rival. He feels responsible for the death. He blames himself and has undue guilt and depression. The feelings associated with this experience may color his future attitudes in competitive situations.

In every chapter previous to the present one on death the emotional problems discussed have all had their origins in emotional disturbances already present in the family group. In the case of the death, especially the death of a parent, the young child is robbed of a need necessary to his development. The blighting and far-reaching emotional effects of death on the young child present one of the few situations in which a totally new factor comes into play and can completely upset the existing parent-child relationships. A parent-child relationship precariously perched on emotional health can succumb to the unleashed and unsatisfied angers and needs created by this new event.

The same general principles apply to the management of the child who has been deserted by a parent or whose parents have been divorced or separated. Do not deny the facts with which the child is already acquainted. Do not dwell at length upon the vices. Do not bring up the subject spontaneously without any questions from the child. Emphasize, without undue lengthy discussions, that the vices were wrong. Above all, do not under any circumstances and for any excuse blame the child for the fact that the other parent left. Children do not break up marriages which are emotionally healthy. The causes of marital conflict usually lie within both marital partners themselves.

Hardly a day went by since the divorce that Mrs. D. did not tell her two little children, "Your daddy left us because he didn't love us anymore." This statement became a constant refrain, being drummed into her children at the slightest provocation and often gratuitously interjected into her conversation. Mrs. D. was an attractive and personable young woman who received many invitations to parties and many requests for dates. But she clung tenaciously to her self-imposed role of the wronged woman. With much ado and even in the presence of her children, she often refused these invitations because, "I would really love to go very much. It gets so lonesome at times. But I must stay home and take care of my two children. . . ." Her mother's repeated offers to babysit for her were always adamantly refused, "I can't ask you to do that for me, Mother. You've already done too much for me." On the rare occasions that Mrs. D. yielded to her friends' entreaties, she spent practically the entire evening telling her escort about her loneliness, the enormous amount of time spent in the care of her children, her previous married life, her divorce and the selfishness and the irresponsibility of her former husband. Such evenings always became propitious occasions for Mrs. D. to unburden her pent-up feelings.

There was the revealing occasion when the children's father, Mr. D., sent each of them a separate Christmas present. The presents arrived through the mail with all the festive wrappings and the usual warnings, "Do not open until Christmas." Mrs. D., without the knowledge of her children, opened the packages, examined the contents and rewrapped the presents. She then went to the store and bought for each child a gift that she knew the child really wanted more than the gift that had been sent by the father. "Your Daddy . . . didn't love us any more."

The two children had numerous emotional problems stemming from the emotional disturbances of the father and the mother that long antedated the marriage and the divorce. As indicated from the above brief example, the divorce did not solve this problem. Mrs. D.'s stormy marriage and subsequent legal solution only provided her with someone to blame for her own inability to adjust and behave in a mature manner.

The court, in its attempt to resolve the parents' conflict over who would receive custody of the children, had decided that the two children would spend 6 months of the year with each parent. The situation already briefly described with the mother was repeated, with a few variations, during the children's stay with the father. The children were caught in a cross fire from which there was no escape. Each parent, without even being aware of the great destructiveness of such behavior, used the children as a means for relieving his or her pent-up hatreds. It should be emphasized again that in most divorces both marital partners are emotionally disturbed; both are responsible for the dissolution of the marriage. And the children seldom escape this family tragedy unscathed.

CHAPTER 21

Adoption: The Problems of Parent and Child

Mr. and Mrs. Jones have been married 10 years and, although they want a baby very much, they have been unable to have one of their own. Their family physician has referred them to a highly reputable adoption agency sponsored by their church. In his letter of introduction to the agency, the physician included a report of the medical history and the excellent physical status of both Mr. and Mrs. Jones. At the agency they were asked many questions and filled out innumerable forms so that as much information as possible could be obtained about their backgrounds—religious, social and economic. Then an appointment was made for them to see the physician with specialized knowledge in the emotional aspects of adoption. He routinely screened potential adoptive parents for the agency. His purpose in the interview was to find out their emotional backgrounds which the agency knew from experience were even more important to the successful rearing of a child than religious, social and economic factors.

After reviewing the records to date, the physician, in a friendly and relaxed atmosphere, asked them many questions about their own parents, brothers and sisters, their own childhoods, adolescences, courtship and marriage. By describing themselves and others close to them, their hopes for their own and the child's future and by asking them to describe their dreams, the physician obtained a clearer picture of the emotional values they attached to the prospective child. From many years of experience in these matters, the physician knew that people often want to adopt children for reasons stemming from sick emotions of their own. He knew the tragic after-math of adopting children for warped emotional reasons.

The physician found that Mr. and Mrs. Jones had no pref-erence for the sex of the baby. They would be happy to re-ceive, love and care for either a boy or a girl. They pictured their child growing up to be a happy, healthy person. Having had good relationships with their own parents and with each other, no other possibility for the child's future occurred to them. The physician knew they would accept and love the child for what he was: a healthy intelligent child with no hereditary diseases and with the potential for growing up to be a very fine person. He knew that warped emotions, exag-gerated fears, hatreds, delinquency, perverted sexuality, in-ability to get along with people, wrecked marriages and other evidences of serious emotional maladjustments are not in-herited from one's parents. They are acquired from the par-ents after birth. A child's virtues or vices are determined by the feelings and the actions of the parents whether such feelings be apparent or concealed. Therefore, the physician was not at all interested in these aspects of the baby's true parents. However, he was greatly interested, and had as nearly complete information as could be obtained, on the existence of any hereditary diseases in the baby's true family.

Finally, after carefully assembling all such information on Mr. and Mrs. Jones, the physician asked them what they would tell the child when he asked them about where he came from. Mr. and Mrs. Jones looked uncertainly at each other, then Mrs. Jones impulsively leaned forward and said, "I'd tell him that we were not his real Mommy and Daddy, that his real Mommy and Daddy were very fine people who loved him very, very much. But they got sick and died and went to heaven. Daddy and I were not able to have a baby of our own, and we wanted a baby to love and to have for our very own. We went to the place where they take care of little babies who have lost their Mommies and Daddies. We looked at many, many babies and when we saw you, we saw how nice you were. We wanted you above all the other babies. We were the happiest people in the world to find such a won-derful baby like you." The physician smiled in a friendly manner. He was not surprised. He had expected an answer such as that. Closing the files on Mr. and Mrs. Jones, he knew they would make fine parents for a little boy or girl.

In contrast with this healthy example was that presented by Mr. and Mrs. Smith and their 7-year-old son, Harry. The Smiths brought Harry to the physician's office because they were at their wit's end and did not know where to turn next. Mr. Smith was a handsome, athletic-looking, well-tailored, manicured man in his early forties. He was very distinguished in his appearance, bearing and self-assurance. He was urbane and cordial to the nurse who escorted the trio into the physician's office. Mrs. Smith, despite her chic clothes and faultlessly applied make-up, did not compare in any sense with her husband. Her facial expression was alert and intelligent, but she was not beautiful. Little Harry was a handsome child with short, curly hair, freckles and finely chiseled features. He was very quiet and shy and remained close to his parents. Harry had set fires in wastepaper baskets at school. The principal had called in the parents and insisted that something be done. He had refused to permit Harry to return to his school until the boy was seen by a physician. Further questioning revealed that this particular act of delinquency had occurred 3 times before, and that there had been repeated interviews between the parents, the teachers and the principal. As part of his complete review of the patient, the physician found that Harry always had had problems suggestive of basic emotional disturbances: breath-holding spells, temper tantrums, marked difficulties with bowel-training, fussy eating habits, prolonged thumb-sucking, bed-wetting, phobias, molesting little girls and, the most recent, fire-setting. Along lines already discussed, the physician found ample evidence that the parents were using Harry as a scapegoat for their own long-standing unresolved emotional problems. However, the feature that distinguished Harry from these previous examples was the excuse that the parents used for making him the scapegoat for their own difficulties. Harry was an adopted child. As such, he was in a particularly vulnerable position. He, as any child might, served as the receptacle and the buffer for all his parent's forbidden destructive feelings and desires. But, as an adopted child, his parents were presented with a convenient excuse. They could blame the specter of Harry's heredity. They could blame Harry's actions on his true parents.

After many years of childless marriage, constant bickering, philandering and trial separations, Mr. and Mrs. Smith's marriage was on the brink of divorce. In final desperation, they decided to seek the advice of the man whose intelligence they respected the most, Mr. Smith's employer. The employer surprised them both by revealing that his only son was adopted, and that his own marriage had been similarly tottering until the adoption brought him and his wife together. The Smiths had casually discussed the possibility of adoption before, but the boss's story convinced them. From this point on, they did not waste any time. Mr. Smith, through his numerous personal connections and business know-how, slashed through all the red tape. They insisted upon a boy, and although they had to wait 2 extra weeks, they got a boy. The agency worker gave the Smiths a brief verbal summary of the boy's family background. The boy's father was a highly successful married business man whose small plant had burned down many years previously. The insurance from this had given him his start in a subsequently successful business enterprise. It was rumored, but never proved, that he had set the fire to his own plant in order to collect the insurance. The boy's mother was a healthy, young, attractive, unmarried woman of Anglo-Saxon background who came to the city with hopes of becoming an actress.

The Smith's reason for adopting the baby was to salvage their marriage which was collapsing because of their mutually faulty emotional relationship. If they wanted a baby very much, the sex of the child would make little difference. They also should have sought the best available medical advice rather than turning to Mr. Smith's employer, who admittedly may have been a fine business man but certainly was no authority on health and disease.

No constructive purpose was served by the agency worker in telling the prospective foster parents about the baby's real parents. The statement that the baby was healthy and that there were no hereditary diseases in the background should have been sufficient.

From the very first, Harry's foster mother feared that Harry would develop some of the moral laxities of his true parents. At the time Harry was adopted, the mother told her husband —and the phrase always remained in her mind—"All these pretty women seem to get into trouble." Then she commented, "What a terrible thing for her parents. If they only knew . . . let's hope Harry never does that to us." She frequently discussed these fears with Mr. Smith. In an attempt to forestall these anticipated problems, Mr. and Mrs. Smith decided to tell Harry the whole truth, as far as they knew it, when he was only 2½ years old. As Mr. Smith said, "There's no sense beating around the bush. The sooner he knows what his parents really were, the better. He might as well face up to the facts. Then he'll appreciate what we're doing for him."

These highly disturbed parents were poor candidates for adoption in the first place. From an extensive study of their lives and feelings, the physician realized that the previous threat of divorce was only another sign of their long-standing individual emotional problems. Without medical help, the chances of these parents raising an emotionally healthy and well-adjusted child were practically nil. Their own emotional disturbances which were being discharged upon each other (and thus leading to divorce), united to find an outlet through their adopted child. A child of such parents, adopted or otherwise, was destined for trouble. The only question was, "How would this come about?" In an adopted child, the excuse of poor heredity is too readily available to the adoptive parents who can thus very easily escape their own responsibility for the child's difficulties. And society, in its lack of knowledge, is too ready to accept such an excuse as plausible. This excuse can be used by the adoptive parents (and accepted by society) whether or not the backgrounds of the true parents are known. In Harry's case, however, an added excuse was unwittingly provided when the adoptive parents were told about the true parents. The foster parents in this case could not only say that heredity would be to blame, but they could say that

heredity was to blame. "Look at Harry's parents. It was rumored that his father got his start in business from fire insurance on a fire he set himself. His mother was just a young
actress. And Harry was illegitimate. What can you expect?"

The sympathy of Mrs. Smith for Harry's true mother (and
therefore for Harry) was not enhanced by her knowledge that
Harry's mother was a beautiful young woman while she herself was plain and middle-aged. Furthermore, Mrs. Smith was
unable to bear children and therefore might have been unsure
of her own femininity in this respect; Harry's true mother had
already shown herself capable of bearing children. In all these
comparisons with Harry's true mother, Mrs. Smith always
came out second best. Such comparisons could only greatly
contribute to Mrs. Smith's already enormous emotional problems. Any anger which she already had from her own life
experiences could only be fortified by such comparisons. It
would be easy for this anger to flare out in a highly destructive
manner against her foster son during one of the innumerable
petty emotional outbursts that often occur between any mother
and child.

For example, during some childish fit of rage, the child who
knows he is adopted, might burst out, "You don't love me!
You're not my real mother anyway! My own mother would
love me!" Here is a ready-made opportunity for the foster
mother (or father) to show her true feelings for the child. If
the foster mother were sure of herself, she would be able to
take the child's temporary angry outburst without a need to
retaliate. She would be sure of her love for her adopted son
and of his love for her. She would know that nothing serious
was meant by the remark or the outburst that led to it. By her
actions and feelings as well as by words she would agree that
his mother loved him very much, but she would also assure
him that she, the foster mother, also loved him very much.
However, in the case of Mrs. Smith, the response would have
differed. Her own underlying anger and guilt toward other
people, toward her adopted son's real mother and toward her
adopted son would cause her to see some frightening truth in
her son's accusation. As a matter of fact, Mrs. Smith actually
lashed back, "Your mother! For your information, your moth-

er was a little no-good tramp! If she loved you, she would
have kept you. You should be grateful you have your Daddy
and me to love you and take care of you."

Any child would feel more secure if he knows he is loved.
Telling him that his true parents left him, because they did
not love him, is very destructive. Any child, as already noted,
also tends to imitate his parents, real and adoptive. Any child,
adopted or not, likes to be proud of his parents. What had
Harry to gain by learning all these destructive things about his
true parents? And what had Harry's foster parents to gain
by learning all these destructive things about Harry's true
parents? They could only gain an excuse for the gratification,
through Harry, of their own destructive emotions. There are
some cases, such as Harry's, in which the real parents did not
love the child and in which the real parents had no traits or
accomplishments of which the child could be proud or which
the child could imitate constructively. How much better
would such a child be served if the adoption agency made an
iron-clad rule to divulge no information on any child's background, other than reassuring the prospective parents that
there are no hereditary diseases in the child's background.
This should be done even if the prospective parents insist on
learning all the details possible about the child's true parents
(and such insistence raises questions about the qualifications
of such people to adopt children). If the child is to develop
in an emotionally healthy manner, he must think well of his
true parents. And if he is to think well of them when the real
parents have no traits or accomplishments of which the child
can be proud, it is to the child's best interests that such knowledge be withheld entirely from both the child and his adoptive
parents. How much better it would be if the adoption agency
were to assume this responsibility in all cases and leave no
possible loopholes in the future relationships between the
child and his prospective adoptive parents.

In Harry's case, the threatened dissolution of his foster
parents' marriage was averted. Harry had served the purpose
for which he was adopted. But this was achieved at the
terrible price of his nearly complete emotional destruction.
The energies of the terrible emotional conflicts of the parents,

which had threatened to destroy the marriage, were shunted from the marriage to Harry.

Related to this problem of the adopted child is the problem of the child who is shifted from foster home to foster home. He never has the time to stay with any family group to identify himself with it and to imitate its grown-ups. And above all and through all is the terrible knowledge that no one loves him and no one cares to keep him.

CHAPTER 22

Hope

Whether the child is emotionally healthy or ill depends mainly upon the basic feelings exchanged between parents and child. The emotions of each generation flow relentlessly to the next. The child reacts to the feelings and the behavior of his parents as they did to the feelings and the behavior of their own parents. When the basic feelings are healthy, good will result; when these feelings are unhealthy, emotional illness will occur. These feelings, which are so important in determining the individual's response to his environment, lie deeply beneath the surface of the individual's personality, and he is often not even aware that they exist. He reacts without knowing why. He may not even realize that he is reacting in a healthy or unhealthy manner. Under the influence of such relentless and hidden forces, he cannot be blamed for his feelings and behavior. But he is responsible for the effects of such feelings and behavior upon his child. Recognizing this parent-child cause-and-effect relationship, the parent whose child is emotionally disturbed should honestly search his own soul. The parent should seek help for both himself and his child. Only then will there be hope.

Index

Blindness, 177
Blood sugar, 90
Body image, 12, 70, 166-167,
    171, 175
    and surgery, 167
Bones, broken, 177
Bottle and nipple, 5, 8, 27, 75
Bottle holder, 2
Bowel, movements, 12-13
    regularity, 13, 65-67
    stage of development, 13-14, 51,
        69, 73, 132
        duration of, 15
        and speech, 75-76
        substitutes for pleasures of,
            13-14, 68-69, 73
    training, 11-13, 70, 76, 82, 194,
        221
Boys, clubs, 31
    feminine, 97, 146
    See also Passivity, Transvestitism
    in girl's clothes, 145-151
Brain, 1, 30, 63, 79-80, 177
    cyst, 190
    disease, 178, 191, 192
    injury, 177, 190, 191, 192
        fear of, 137
    tumor, 90
        and obesity, 62
    wave studies, 1, 90
Breath-holding, 88, 89-90, 121
Bribery, 4, 8, 207
Bruxism, 14
Bullying, 49-50, 77, 82, 121, 148,
    167
Burns, 167, 176-177

Cajolery, 4
Cancerophobia, 107
Career woman, 49, 109
Castration anxiety, 139, 147, 171
    and dental work, 169
    in girl, 168
    and hair cuts, 169
    and nose, throat and mouth, 169
Cathartics, 13, 65-67
Catheterization, 169

Children, beating, 55
    forcing, 8
    guidance center, 104
    model, 58, 109
    position in family setting, 128
    ward, 162
Church, 121
    and conscience, 119
Circumcision, 135, 169, 171
Clay-modeling, 14
Cleanliness, 11, 13, 72, 142
Cleft palate, 177
Clubbed foot, 177
Coaxing of child, 8
Colitis, ulcerative, chronic, 33,
    73-74, 193
Comics, 17, 115
Communication methods, chance
        remarks, 192
    constant checking, 124-125
    covert permission, 41, 116,
        142-143, 146
    distortion, 32
    double standards of conduct,
        117-120, 147, 151
    double talk, 117
    doubts, 32, 123-124, 135,
        142-143, 155, 213-214
    dreams, 34-35
    exaggerated behavior, 30,
        123-124, 163
    facial expression, 32, 116, 125-148
    failure to censure, 211
    failure to comment, 32, 141,
        148-150
    fait accompli, 123
    half-smiles, 32, 116
    insinuation, 31-32, 124-125
    knowledge of heredity, 222
    play, 33-34
    preoccupation, 164, 213-214
    rapt interest, 32, 116-117, 125,
        135-136
    secretly following, 147
Compulsions, 80
    age when often seen, 80
Concentration difficulty, 7

4   R/ 7ILMC

              Schwatz